GREAT WAR
1898

TOTAL WAR

BOOK 2

JACK MOORE

Trench Foot

In March of 1900, Cordell Hull was a twenty-eight year old Captain of the Tennessee Volunteers. Since the war had started in November of 1898, he had spent most of his time working in Nashville at the Judge Advocate General's Office of the State of Tennessee's War Department Headquarters. Hull was an attorney by trade, but that had been in the civilian world. He had only gone to law school after he did his time in the military. Like most white men in the Confederacy, he did a prolonged stint in the reserves. After his time as a private soldier in a standing Tennessee infantry regiment, he received a second lieutenant's commission not long after graduating from college. His military service was completed several years before the war began, but like most men in Tennessee, he volunteered to serve again.

For Hull, serving was more than just a patriotic gesture. He had been born and raised in Pickett County. He was not old enough to remember the first war against the United States, but it had shaped his entire life at a very personal

1

level. Pickett County sat on the international border, and the US state of Kentucky was, quite literally, only a shouting distance from Hull's home. There were always Confederate troops in Pickett County who were there to work on the border fortifications. People in Hull's hometown lived with the fear that the "damn Yankees" would one day return.

By March of 1900, that fear had been realized and as Hull worked in a lawyer's office, safely in the state capital, it was with the knowledge that his home and family were living under the rule of US Military Law. There were many stories about how cruel the occupational authorities were, and while Hull was an educated man and must have realized that many of these stories were just war time propaganda, he had to have the sneaking suspicion that a good number of these tales had at least a grain of truth to them. This must have been why Hull was not content to spend the rest of the war working behind a desk.

It did not take much for Hull to get his wish. As the war dragged on, and 1899 turned into 1900, the only thing that was really required to go to the front was just to ask. The fact that Hull found himself commanding a company from the 16th Texas Rifles is testimony to that. Before the war, it was rare to have men from two separate states in the same unit, let alone commanding a company. By 1900, when Confederate units were rotated off the line, there was usually a mad scramble for those units to replace losses and the competitions to fill those positions were fierce. When a man like Hull volunteered to serve in your unit, then you took him no matter what state he was from. When Hull reported to his new unit that was refitting near Huntingdon, he would find that he was far from the only non-Texan there. In fact, most of the replacements were not from Texas, and there was even one man from England.

Hull would spend six weeks with B Co 1/16 TRR, training, getting to know his people, and settling in before they would be put back on the line just north of Fort Bragg, Tennessee. That was not to say that he was ready for the job, just yet. In Hull's wartime memoirs, he made no secret of the fact that he was not ready. He still had time to learn some critical lessons before they became life or death.

As time went on, the men who really ran B Company would finally allow him to really be the commanding officer, but that was only because they had also been allowed the time to learn him and judge his worth.

The war time memoirs of Cordell Hull have been an invaluable aid to many historians. He gave a very candid and unpolished account of the average life of Johnny Kudzu. It's very interesting to compare his writing to that of another army captain by the name of Woodbury Kane. Their writings make it sound as if they had served in the same unit, but they not only served in different units but in different armies.

Kane was a bit older than Hull. By March of 1900, he was already past 40 and considered well beyond military age. His initial service was as a Second Lieutenant in the United States Army. After his tour was up, he seems to have not given the military a second glance. Kane was originally from Rhode Island but had lived in New York City a good many years before the war. He was Harvard educated and friends with a good many influential people, including

Theodore Roosevelt.

Kane was quite the sportsman and probably the poster child for Victorian manhood. He boxed, fenced, hunted, and spent most of his life doing what we would now describe as extreme sports. Why he volunteered for service when the war began is a mystery, but given his past, it would almost seem as if he really did view the war as an adventure. Unlike Hull, Kane would actually have to fight to get back in the army, let alone get reinstated as an officer. It would take a letter to his friend, Theodore Roosevelt, to finally get it.

Kane would spend nearly a year as one of many aides on the staff of Major General Charles Wikoff, who commanded the US 24th Infantry Division in upstate New York. By all accounts, Kane did not get along with Wikoff very well. Kane never spoke of it, but a pre-war friend of his that also worked on Wikoff's staff, by the name of Hamilton Fish, did make a passing reference to it in his journal. Unfortunately, Fish would be killed before the end of the war, and his various papers never became a cohesive work.

It does appear likely that Kane did not get along with the General. Kane's service during the war showed a definite pattern of on-going problems with superior officers. Even so, Kane was promoted to Captain while serving with Wikoff, although this may or may not say much. It is a common practice in many bureaucracies to promote someone in order to get rid of them. There is no way to know for sure, but we do know that Kane was transferred to the 69th New York Infantry Regiment in the late autumn of 1899. He was not there long before he took command of E Company.

This is where the differences between Hull and Kane become more pronounced, although these differences had little to do with the day to day tedium that is the life of any soldier in any army. When Hull took over his command, he was in a rear area. Kane took command of E company while it was serving on the front lines near Saint-Remi, Quebec. His only saving grace, if you can call it that, was the fact that it was winter, and the hostilities were at a minimum. The way the US Army replacement system worked, it would not have made any difference

what time of year it was. This just
happened to be when the position came
open, and, as per the doctrine of the time,
Kane filled it.

Kane spent much of that winter
learning how to stay warm. While this
might sound like humor, in reality, the
cold was every bit as deadly as the
Canadians. While many US soldiers did
come from climates that were as cold as
Quebec, there is a distinct difference
between spending the winter in a civilian
home and surviving, exposed, in a trench,
where something warm like a fire can flag
you for an enemy artillery strike. It takes
a special set of skills to survive under
those conditions and, as Kane would find
out, many of the veterans were unwilling
to pass along the lessons they had learned
from the previous winter. He was the
company commander, and if they were
willing to ignore him, then it was for
certain that new privates entering the line
would be equally lost.

This was becoming a problem
across the front lines, and it was mainly
due to the replacement system that the US
Army had adopted. The veterans had
seen too many friends die and, as a result,

most did not wish to become emotionally invested in some new guy that may or may not last a week. It was a system that fed on itself in that the replacements might have had a much better chance of survival had someone taken the time to teach them the things that they needed to know. This system meant replacements always took, at least, fifty percent higher casualties than the veterans. and problems like winter survival were elevated from a surmountable obstacle to a near certain death trap.

Despite being twice as old as the average soldier, Kane had been an exceptional athlete for most of his life and was in good shape. He survived till spring and by the time the tempo of operations began to accelerate, he had proven his worth to the key members of his company and earned a certain measure or respect. He was also lucky enough to survive his first battles as the US Army resumed its offensive towards Montreal. By the time these engagements were over with he would be a veteran and not because he had become an expert. It was due to the sea of new faces that would flood E Co as replacements for those who had died between the trenches in one charge after another.

Kane was appalled by this and he hid nothing in his correspondence with his old friend Roosevelt. These letters have survived to this day, in the Roosevelt Collection, so we have ample firsthand evidence, and the tone is not one of a disenfranchised soldier who is only complaining. There is no doubt that Kane was far from the only company commander who was starting to notice one or two things, but in this case, we have a clear record. Here, we know that Kane began thinking about how to avoid the mass slaughter around him. One thing is very clear in his correspondence, he was positive that it could be avoided.

Attrition

One thing is very much for certain. Woodbury Kane was far from the only person who was thinking about how to avoid the mass slaughter that the great powers now found themselves involved in. One such individual was Garnet Wolseley, 1st Viscount Wolseley,

Commander-in-Chief of Forces, which is a fancy way of saying he was the chief of staff of the British Army and the highest-ranking military man in Britain. He had spent his entire war at Pall Mall, headquarters of the British Army. Of all the men in similar positions around the world, it seems that Wolseley and his staff were the first to realize the exact nature of the situation that they were in.

Wolseley's boss, Robert Gascoyne-Cecil, the Earl of Salisbury, was the current Prime Minister of Great Britain. Lord Salisbury had a long career in civil service and was a well-known conservative who, also had the ability to compromise. He was an expert in foreign affairs and his record long indicated that he truly believed one of his more famous sayings. Maybe it is quite ironic that this saying was, "whatever happens will be for the worse, so it is in our best interests to make sure nothing happens." Some have suggested that his "let it be" attitude helped contribute to the start of the war, but those were now days past.

Since 1899, Lord Salisbury had been really waging two wars, the military and the political. The first was to defeat the enemies of Great Britain and the second was to keep his job. Ironically it would be Kitchener's Mozambique campaign that would ultimately leave Salisbury at Ten Downing, although, many things about his third tenure as Prime Minister would greatly change. It was not the fact that Kitchener had delivered a much needed, and widely popular, victory. It was largely because the ensuing crisis, one that would play out behind closed doors, made even Salisbury's most avid critics realize that this was no time for internal squabbles. As a result, Salisbury's already "compromise cabinet," would become even more so as Great Britain got an emergency war council that would govern till the end of the war.

In February and March of 1900, this cabinet was just starting to sort itself out with endless meetings that were largely devoted to structuring the details of Britain's wartime economy. They had yet to really call it that and, there is some question if the men who were doing this work even realized that was exactly what they were doing. It seems more plausible that they had just taken up the work that was obviously right in front of them and had yet to fully appreciate the larger picture. It would be Garnet Wolseley who would put it all in perspective for them.

There was one other serious, and quite unofficial, change. It was an open secret at White Hall, but no one would speak much of it and no reporters, obviously, felt inclined to print the story. The fact was that Lord Salisbury was in failing health and while he remained Prime Minister the truth of the matter was that he had less and less to do with the daily managing of the government or the war. Many of these duties had slowly been taken over by his nephew, another career politician, by the name of Arthur Balfour.

It was in this climate that Wolseley gave the cabinet the news. For the better part of a year, Wolseley had formed a special section that many at Pall Mall just referred to as "Statistics." This term was a euphemism of the day and quite often translated into "spies." There was intelligence work going on in this section, but these men really were looking at statistics and crunching numbers. A good deal of their information was from the pre-war period but given the data they were most interested in it was unlikely that much of it had changed over the course of the past few years. Wolseley read everything coming out of that section, on a daily basis, and by the time he delivered the full report to the cabinet, at their meeting of the 21st of February, he was as familiar with the report as anyone could be. He had also reached one inescapable conclusion.

The details of the report were certainly no secret to anyone. All of it was information that was widely known before the war. The difference was that no one had ever condensed this information, in this way, and presented it in this framework. Wolseley noted after three days of presenting it to the cabinet, that the Secretaries were growing more and more restless. If the writings of Joe Chamberlin can be believed, it was not because Wolseley was handing them news of imminent defeat. Curiously, he was not telling them of certain victory either. What truly disturbed the leaders of Great Britain was that he could not predict any outcome based on the information they had.

Strangely enough, and a bit too late,

what Wolseley realized, even then, was that he had also stumbled over the cause of the war. He did not stress this to the cabinet, but he did bring it up because it was relevant to the situation that they now faced. The reason for the war was a set of numbers and this set was far simpler than the endless pages of data sitting in front of them. It was because of something that Otto Von Bismarck had realized in decades past. He had used this to keep the peace in Europe, but something unseen had come along and upset this formula.

In the pre-war world, there were five nations considered to be the great powers. Those were Great Britain, Germany, France, Russia, and Austria-Hungary. When even the most divisive of issues arose between the powers, the simple math was that one side would always be larger. There would always be a three to two margin and the side with the two would always have to back down. Bismarck had cleverly figured this out and made sure that Germany was always on the side of the three. What no one had realized, through the eighties and nineties, was that this basic formula of peace had changed. There was another player on the board, and no one seemed to have recognized this basic fact.

You could call it simple human oversight or, quite possibly prejudice. I'm of the opinion that it was most likely both. Maybe the politicians of Europe did not include the US in their calculations simply because the US was not European. They were an ocean and how could they possibly effect, or even care, about the affairs of Europe? It never seems to have crossed the minds of European leaders that they had been dabbling in North American affairs for centuries. Why would the Americans not return the favor when they finally had the ability? Europe seemed to have failed to connect US desires with the fact that the world was getting smaller.

After the United States lost its first war with the Confederacy it had all but abandoned it's long running policy of isolation. This was not something that the men in the cabinet were unaware of, in fact, anyone who read the newspapers knew this. The United States had an abundance of raw materials and a population that was rapidly expanding. There was certainly nothing new or secret

15

about that. What the US had after the American 61, that they did not before, was a desire to harness that energy and a purpose with which to direct it.

As a result of this drastic change, in the late 19th century, the number of players on the board had changed. Now there were six great powers and because no one recognized this basic fact, the ensuing crisis of September 1898, led to neither faction backing down. Each nation was completely confident that it had the numbers on its side. This was relevant in the early spring of 1900, to Wolseley at least, because it would now dictate how the war would have to be prosecuted. The news was not well received.

The simple fact, that Wolseley's statisticians had put into perspective, was that the appearance of strength shared by each alliance was no illusion. Up till this point, the militaries of the world had failed to deliver any substantial victories on the battlefield and, at this point, it was doubtful that they ever would. That left the two great alliances locked in a war of attrition. Put simply, this was now a contest of who would run out of resources first. This is what greatly upset the cabinet because who had the most was simply too close to call.

Each nation, in each alliance, had their own strengths and weaknesses. On the whole, these largely canceled each other out. It left the Allies (Britain, Germany, and Austria-Hungary) and the Triple Entente (France, Russia, and the United States) in a dead heat and virtually identical across the board. Their access to raw materials, the fire power of their armies, the viability of their fleets, the production capabilities of their factories, and the size of their populations were so close that it was impossible to say who had the most of what and where.

This news presented in this fashion only set off a heated round of debate among the cabinet members. As Chamberlin would later write, "they wanted him (Wolseley) to tell them that a day of jubilance or apocalypse was right around the corner and he gave them the truth instead." Indeed, Wolseley proved that admitting one's own ignorance is, more times than not, the most difficult thing to do. Many in the cabinet even went so far as to ask the question of

Wolseley, "then what good are you?"

Wolseley did not come up short on this matter. He had realized, some time before, that human endurance would not allow the conflict to continue until there was nothing left of anything. One side or the other was going to break long before that happened. While this much seems obvious, Wolseley pointed out that even the breakdown of each alliance would not happen all at once. He coined the term, "decision points" and stated that there would be a series of them ahead. The first trick was to recognize them for what they were and, after that, the side that would claim victory would be the one who handled these points the best.

The reception of this theory was no better received than the rest of the news. It became controversial from the moment that Wolseley presented it and, in many ways, it remains so until this very day. No matter what the opinion was of each secretary, the one thing they would not do during the war at least was speak a word of this report outside of the cabinet. In fact, the work of Wolseley's military math gurus would remain top secret for many decades to come. It would not see the public light of day until long after the men in that room were all dead and gone.

In some ways, at least to historians, it is somewhat tragic that this report remained so secret for so long. Many opinions of Wolseley's term as Chief of Staff, along with Lord Salisbury's handling of the war, might have been judged quite differently by earlier historians. No matter what you think of the report, and it's very cold and callous nature, one thing about it is undisputed. Wolseley was right and the first of his "decision points" was less than a month away.

The Neutrals

"There is no greater an excuse than victory," was a term that was penned by Winston Churchill. While he wrote of this long after the war, there are very few who doubt that it was his time serving in the army of Horatio Kitchener that led him to this conclusion. The reasons should be more than obvious and the one example that shines above all others is Kitchener's invasion of the neutral Portuguese territory of Mozambique. His victory over the Boers, as well as his disruption of their supply lines, did result in the lifting of the sieges of the British border posts in South Africa. As Kitchener had predicted, while he proposed his adventure to his fellow officers, the Portuguese did not respond to the violation of their territory.

On the surface, Kitchener pulled off quite a coup and was even more popular, back home, than ever before. Indeed, Portugal not only failed to respond, but they bent over backwards to make sure they would not have to. The reality was that Portugal had very little control over their colony that was managed exclusively by a private corporation with a royal charter. One of the most lasting effects of Kitchener's invasion was that Portugal would eventually revoke the charter of the Mozambique Company, but during the war this meant very little. The corporation was in the habit of ignoring edicts from Lisbon and they did so once again. The entire matter would not be settled till many years after the war. For the time being, in Mozambique it was business as usual.

The more important factor was the pre-war perception of Portugal being a puppet of Great Britain. While it is very true that the British had considerable influence in Lisbon, they were not as in control as it appeared but, unfortunately, in politics sometimes appearances are all that matter. What Kitchener did not seem to take into account, and his bosses realized, was that the fallout from invading neutral territory went well beyond Anglo-Portuguese relations. It is ironic that Kitchener's complete disregard for the complexity of the situation is probably what saved his command more than even his popularity at home.

Since the outset of hostilities, both alliances were engaged in a furious diplomatic war to coax the world's neutral states to either commit to their cause, or at the least, deny their resources to the other. So far, Britain had been slowly winning this conflict. The Confederate States were already involved in a pre-war military alliance with Great Britain, so, there was never any question that the CSA would go to war. The Confederacy was not a world power, but they were a regional one and crucial to British defense plans in North America.

Britain also managed to coax another regional power into the conflict, very early on. Japan was proving to be just as critical in the Pacific where British forces had experienced an early string of military setbacks. Meanwhile, Austria-Hungary had managed to coax Imperial Mexico into the war and gave the United States yet another front to fight on. Finally, there was the Turkish Ottoman Empire. Even before the war it was rapidly destabilizing, and the onset of hostilities had not helped. It had begun the conflict on the side of France even if it was waging an unofficial war against France's ally, Russia. Kitchener's defeat of the "Young Turk" army in the Sinai had caused a factional shift, put the Sultan back in power, and caused Turkey to switch sides.

The advantages of these diplomatic victories were long since spent. The CSA failed to achieve their prewar objectives and were now locked in a grinding fifteen-hundred-mile-long siege with its larger northern neighbor. Japan was equally bogged down in a stagnant, and quite bloody, battle with Russo-American forces on the Korean peninsula. If anything, Japan was now proving to be more of a liability to Britain, than an asset.

The Pacific Fleet of the Royal Navy was now almost exclusively engaged in operations to safeguard the supply lines of a resource poor Japan, not to mention, supporting the Meiji Government's armies on the Asian continent. Japan had been building up their own fleet, but it had not yet grown to the size they truly needed. Their capital prewar vessels were, also, almost exclusively secondhand vessels that had been retired from the Royal Navy. No such vessels were now for sale and this left Japan hopelessly dependent on Britain for the rest of the war.

Most other countries had done their best to avoid becoming embroiled in the conflict. Some, such as Denmark, had even quietly ignored the blatant violations of their territorial neutrality. In this particular case it was the establishment of small British outposts in Greenland that were used to aid shipping that attempted to run the American blockade of Canada.

The Mozambique invasion would cause
this situation to turn critical for little
Denmark, and several other nations
besides.

The violation of Portuguese
territory put many of these neutral
powers in a very awkward position. It
drove home the point that their only
recourse, to such military adventures as
Kitchener's, was to join one of the two
belligerent alliances and that was the
situation they were ultimately trying to
avoid. Their only other option was to
accept the violation of their territories or
possessions, and in most cases domestic
politics would not allow for this. Most of
these small nations had hawk and dove
factions like in any other nation and
Kitchener had inadvertently caused a
shift in nearly all of these, the world over.

As with the case of Denmark, a
nation that had quite possibly the
strongest of dove factions, it put them
directly in the cross hairs of the
belligerent powers. Denmark found they
could no longer ignore British activity in
and around Greenland. There was very
little that they could do about it militarily
but, their strategic position on the Baltic

and closer ties with France and Russia could threaten Britain's ally, Germany. The Kaiser did not wait for that to happen and before summer German troops were marching into Denmark. The Danes did not resist the occupation of their country and, curiously enough, they did not even declare war on anyone. They quietly accepted German occupation for the time being.

In Britain, the German invasion was not met with great fanfare and caused even more headaches for the Salisbury Cabinet. It also complicated an even more sensitive situation with the Netherlands that also shared a common border with Germany. Both sides were very interested in the Netherlands, but not so much for their status as a continental power since, in that respect, they were anything but. Holland's single biggest asset was her colonies and, in particular, Indonesia. Not only did the Dutch East Indies hold a strategic position in the South Pacific, but they were also a major producer of many raw goods that were highly coveted by both sides. The most important of these was rubber.

The invasion of Denmark caused Holland to threaten suspension of diplomatic ties with Germany, however, they subtly suggested that they did not wish to take a belligerent line with the Anglo-German alliance. The Netherlands did not threaten to suspend relations with any of Germany's allies and this was a clear sign that they intended to keep walking the same tight rope that they had been. It was a situation that London could live with until it became clear that other required actions might push Holland into the Triple Entente.

This weighed heavily on the minds of the Salisbury Government. Holland did not have much of an army to bring to the table and the German's could most likely, very easily, stomp the country flat in a matter of weeks. It would not matter, because Britain would be forced to divert valuable resources in order to neutralize Indonesia and secure her precious rubber plantations. It would also, undoubtedly, lead to the involvement of yet another neutral power that Britain and Germany wished to keep that way.

Where Holland's strategic position gave her negotiating power, Belgium found that her position was having the opposite effect. Indeed, before the war, Von Schlieffen had argued for a flanking attack through Belgium in order to defeat the French. While Schlieffen had ultimately been overruled by his rival Waldersee, this did not mean that such ideas were confined only to Germany. The French had also toyed with the idea of invading Belgium, but up until now, had failed to do so for a variety of reasons.

President For Life Boulanger had chosen to run his nation from his military headquarters at the Sedan. He only traveled back to Paris (and anywhere else for that matter) if it was absolutely necessary. His Generals had been visiting the headquarters and feverishly arguing with Boulanger about invading Belgium. Many of these men were the same Generals commanding the armies that could not break the German defenses around Metz and Strasbourg.

There were merits to the French Generals' arguments and concerns. The Franco-German border at Alsace-Loraine was very small and the geography did not allow the French to mass enough troops in front of either fortified city in order to make a decisive attack. The small nature of the theater, all by itself, also allowed the Germans to use a minimal number of troops to hold back all of France's army. This meant that the Germans were free to concentrate the bulk of their armies against France's ally, Russia. An invasion of Belgium would not only allow a flanking attack on the city of Metz, but it would force the Germans to commit more resources to a larger front.

In this matter, Georges Boulanger showed an uncharacteristic amount of pragmatism. His argument seems to be perfectly valid as well, and it all hinged around, once again, geography. An invasion of Belgium would open up a larger front, but this advantage was largely offset by the terrain. The German-Belgium border was a region consisted of heavily forested hills that were known as the Ardennes. It was the perfect terrain for slowing down an army and defending. The Germans had easier access to the region, and Boulanger feared the Germans would overrun the area before his own troops could.

The only advantage that would be

had by a Franco invasion of the low countries would be if Holland were invaded in conjunction with Belgium. The low flat terrain of southwestern Holland would be ideal for marching around the German flank and into their industrial heartland, the Ruhr River Valley. Unfortunately, once again, terrain was not working in France's favor. Here it was a simple matter of distance. The Germans were ultimately closer, and in this scenario, they would not have to fight through the Belgian defenses at Liege and Antwerp. Once this picture evolved, as Boulanger saw it, he would also be facing the same strategic nightmare as his British enemies. That would be the task of having to subdue the Dutch East Indies. So, for now, he would only invade Belgium if Holland joined the war on the side of the Triple Entente first.

Again, the Mozambique situation was threatening to change the very balance of the war in theaters far from its shores. The only saving grace was that most of the smaller powers in Europe were doing their best to keep both sides pleased and by extension, maintain their neutral status. It was becoming increasingly difficult in the post

Mozambique environment. Of course, that was only in northwestern Europe. There were other neutrals who were only biding their time and waiting for the right opportunity to enter the war. The side they would choose had little to do with sympathies and more to do with how much they could get for their efforts.

The Wild Cards

The allegiance of smaller nations was only important to the belligerents for either their strategic positions or raw materials. With the total preoccupation of the great powers of the world, how these smaller nations would fair basically came down to how well they played their cards. Some would become very rich, either by luck or skill, while others would suffer. By 1900, there were not many nations left who possessed forces that were capable of altering the military situation.

The only nations that were outside of Europe and harbored ambitions with enough military power to possibly accomplish those ambitions, were in

South America. Specifically, it was Argentina and Brazil and they had been antagonists for nearly a century. Argentina was doing quite well, during the first few years of the war, selling wheat and beef to both sides at a price that went up in value almost every month. They were coming under increasing pressure by the British to embargo the Tripple Entente. The Argentinians also had their own separate issues with the US and France. To sum up their situation, they easily had excuses to go to war with either side and they had considerable naval assets that, with the exception of Brazil, were unchecked on the South American continent.

One might think that Argentina had a good thing going with a literal cash cow of products that were desperately sought by both sides. Because of this they felt only minor diplomat pressure from the belligerents with both sides afraid of offending them too greatly. Apparently, this was not good enough for Argentina. In truth, the hawks (those calling for war) had greatly outnumbered the doves (those who wished to stay out of it) by a considerable margin and this had been the case since the start of the war.

Argentina's fundamental reason for sitting on the side lines was that they couldn't figure out which side they wanted to be on. This was the primary debate in Buenos Aries, and it was as furious as war or peace in other capitals.

The main reason for this quandary was that while they hated the British intensely, the Argentinians had an equally strong working relationship with Britain's chief ally, Germany. There was a sizable German population that lived in Argentina and, unlike similar immigrants in the United States, these Germans were very much pro mother country. Argentina was also a favorite pre-war vacation spot for wealthy Germans and, as such, relations between the two countries could not have been better.

It was the Mozambique Expedition that ultimately settled the matter and on March 3rd, 1900 the anti-British faction finally won out. Argentina declared it's resolve to reclaim the Molvina Islands that were currently a British protectorate called the Falklands. The ownership of these islands were a long running dispute between the two nations that was virtually unknown outside of Argentina. Even in

Britain, you would be hard pressed to find an average citizen on the streets who had ever heard of the place. Still, the ownership of these islands was the basis of Argentina's entire declaration of war which, appeared to be quite limited. They did not declare war on any of Britain's allies nor did they make any offers to cooperate with any of Britain's enemies.

If this was a plan to placate Argentina's native German population it ultimately failed. Great Britain already had plans, on the board, for this eventuality and had long since consulted her allies over the matter. Germany was in agreement that if the Triple Entente were to get coaling bases in this region then it could be a disaster. US and French cruisers were already causing enough problems without a base, so by the 5th of March, the entire Anglo-German alliance declared war on Argentina and put them squarely in the Franco-American camp. The European immigrants of Argentina were not happy with this and would remain a problem for the rest of the war. This would cause rifts and political instability that has lasted in Argentina to this very day.

It is worthy to note that the situation in South America was very similar to that in the North. While the American 61 raged between the US and CS, Argentina began acting on plans that would unify and industrialize their nation, with the ultimate goal of emerging as a first world power. This had put them squarely at odds with their large northern neighbor, the Empire of Brazil. The result would be several wars that were every bit as devastating as the one being fought by their English-speaking neighbors to the north. It would also result in a continued arms race between Argentina and Brazil.

Unlike Argentina, there was never any debate in Brazil about which alliance was favored. If Argentina had entered the war on the Anglo-German side, then it is likely that Brazil would have stayed out of the conflict entirely. The reason for this was that Brazil and the Confederate States enjoyed a very close strategic partnership. Wealthy Confederate businessmen owned extensive holdings in Brazil and each nation enjoyed favored trade status with the other. Almost continual meddling by the US, in internal Brazilian affairs, had only served to strengthen the ties with the Confederacy.

Since the war first broke out, Brazil had failed to go to war, but then again, she had never really been asked. Even so, Brazil was not technically neutral since they openly declared their support for their North American allies.

The only thing, in Brazil, that was possibly stronger than her relations with the Confederacy was her animosity towards Argentina. Brazilians saw the upstart nation as a genuine threat and, in part, this seems to be a great deal of the reason why Brazil kept strong ties with the CSA. When the Confederacy declared war on Argentina in response to the declaration against Britain, there was never any question or debate in Brazil about what she would do.

Brazil would enter the war by the 8th of March and now South America would share in the horrors that were already being experienced in Europe, North America, and Asia. Before it would be over with the smaller nations of Uruguay and Paraguay (the latter of whom had yet to recover from the last war) would be caught up in this conflict and one of them would eventually cease to exist. Indeed, it is easy to argue that no matter how much damage had been done elsewhere in the world, ultimately, South America would suffer more than anyone else. The war would redraw the map in South America and shatter long range plans and reforms that had been the order of the day in the pre-war world.

While the war would have major ramifications for those who lived in South America, the truth of the matter was, it was not a serious concern to the great powers. They had more than enough trouble of their own, and while the region was important for one or two reasons, it was far from vital to the larger conflict. At the time, there was only one nation left that remained uncommitted and had resources that both sides not only coveted, but considered crucial.

The Italians

The main reason for this is because Italy was in Europe and held the ability to the tip the balance of power in the western Mediterranean. That region was not only crucial to both sides, but it was still largely up for grabs. Italy could easily decide the question, and, quite possibly, even force a major sea battle that the civilian governments of both sides were trying to avoid.

The respective navies were, if nothing else, desirous and spoiling for another fight. Many naval officers had studied the Battle of the Yellow Sea and were confident they could correct the mistakes and produce a major victory for their side. Their political leadership was not so optimistic in their appraisal, but ultimately it would not matter. What had been equally recognized in the war rooms around the word was that with the attempt of winning a major victory came the risk of catastrophic defeat. The simple fact was that the Admirals could not guarantee a victory with any degree of certainty and gambling the entire war on a single throw of the dice was seen as too risky.

Despite attempts by both sides to close off the western Mediterranean, shipping was still getting through. The area was equally important to both Britain and France. Much like their plans for an African railroad, these interests intersected in this particular body of water. Britain's all too crucial shipping lanes to the Suez, and ultimately India, required east/west travel. France was equally dependent on her commerce with her African colonies, primarily through the port of Oran, in Algeria. The French lanes ran along a north/south route from there to Marseilles.

Despite having the initial advantages, France was slowly losing the contest for control of the western Mediterranean. The Royal Navy had collected a heavy toll for the use of those waters, but despite this, they had yet to stop the traffic between the two continents. France had dealt out considerable pain on the British convoys that "ran the gauntlet", as Merchant Marines called it. This was generally considered the final leg of the journey from Sicily to Gibraltar. More British ships would go down in that area, than anywhere else in the world.

While the Kingdom of Italy was not considered a formidable military power, and rightly so, the addition of her Navy to anyone's war effort could easily tip the balance in one of the most hotly contested and crucial theaters of war. This was a fact that the Italians were only too aware of. What made this situation so dangerous, for both sides in the war, was the volatile nature of domestic Italian politics that had combined, in the pre-war era, with an overly ambitious plan for colonial expansion.

One must understand that Italian foreign policy was generated more by her domestic problems as opposed to any vague desire to rekindle the Roman Empire. Italy was a nation that was at war with itself in every way imaginable. She was internally divided in politics by radical republicans on one side and hard-core monarchists on the other. She was divided geographically by a rapidly industrializing north and a primarily agricultural south that, in the past four decades, had known over population that combined with one failed harvest after another. All nations knew such problems, but in Italy the various factional leaders tended to be radical. There seemed to be little room for compromise.

In 1900, the kingdom was only four decades old, and many Italians did not even consider themselves as subjects. Their loyalties were generally elsewhere, and foreign powers, most notably France and Austria-Hungary, had taken full advantage of these divisions. The only possible unifying force on the entire peninsula was the Catholic Church. Even in the realm of religion, generally a very strong factor for unity, this proved to be far more divisive.

The Papacy was seen as a French puppet, and, indeed, the French had occupied Rome up until the Franco Prussian War of 1871. The removal of those troops had set the Vatican and the new Italian Monarchy on a collision course. These issues had not been settled in 1900 and would not be for some time to come. Still, if the problems with the French were bad, relations with Austria-Hungary were even worse.

Trieste was a city on the Adriatic Sea and one of the few good ports in that region. It was a crossroads city with a multi-ethnic population that would have been trouble enough all by itself. What made the city a sore point was that it also happened to be the only good port that the Hapsburg Monarchy of Austria-Hungary owned. Without it, the Austro-Hungarian Empire became a land-locked nation, cut off from the world and destined to obscurity. Losing this city was not a situation that either Franz Joseph in Vienna, or his staunch ally Kaiser Wilhelm, could live with.

Italy also claimed control of the city, but currently she did not own it. It was the stubborn Italian claims that forced Franz Joseph to dabble in internal Italian politics, primarily for the security of his one and only port. The Italians resented this, and, as they saw it, the only way to protect themselves from the Hapsburg regime was to become a world empire. This seemed to be the only way that they thought they could achieve the power required to deal with the Austrians as equals, but as of 1900 their entire foreign policy had been a complete and unqualified disaster.

Italy found that it was not powerful enough to build a colonial empire on its own. It required the ascent and active aid of the larger powers, most of whom they had gone out of their way to alienate at one time or another. They had gotten swept up by the Anglo-French competition to build the trans-African railroad, and this led Italy to war in 1895.

At the urging of the British, based on plans to keep the French from establishing bases in Eastern Africa, Italy attempted to conquer the independent nation of Abyssinia (modern day Ethiopia). With Russian material aid, the Ethiopians soundly defeated the Italians. (The same Ethiopian Army would later force Bonchamps to give up his expedition and directly lead to the war.)

The memory of this humiliating defeat was still fresh on the minds of Italians in 1900. Strangely enough, it was not a deterrent to war, but it was actually a key factor in making Italian entry in the larger conflict inevitable. This was true of both Italian leaders and the populace. The leadership, in both factions, understood that cementing a national character through military victories was essential to a modern Italy. The average Italian was a very prideful person, even by European standards of the time, and wanted the Abyssinian stain erased from the record. By 1900, there were many calls to invade Abyssinia once more, and with the Great Powers being distracted, the time seemed right.

The only real thing preventing an

African adventure was the Italian Government's understanding of exactly what was at stake for them. So far, Italy's choices had been dismal at best. Their African adventure, while serving their own interests, were largely made possible because they were similar to those of Britain. On the continent, their alliance with Germany was only because it kept both, Austria Hungary and France, from doing any serious meddling in domestic Italian affairs. Neither of these temporary alliances were ideal for Italy, and, as the Italian government correctly saw it, the only way they would ever be free to make their own choices was the course they had set. They would establish their own empire.

This was a high stakes gambit for Italy. If they chose the right side in this war, then they could easily walk away with the empire they so coveted and maybe even more besides. This would go far in politically stabilizing the country and they would finally be on a firm path to real unity, something they had yet to truly accomplish. This was a popular notion with every faction of the radicalized Italian political landscape. They had to choose wisely though.

The pitfalls were just as great. If Italy wound up on the losing side of the war, then it might mean more than just military defeat. It might even mean more than just a shift in power bases among the host of political factions. It might even mean more than just the downfall of the government and the monarchy. A defeat in this war could easily lead to the collapse of the entire nation and open the peninsula up to foreign domination. This would result in another collection of patchwork states who were constantly at war with each other. That was all Italy had been from practically the fall of the Roman Empire until the mid-19th century, and nobody wanted to see it return. Even so, it was still a very real possibility.

This was why, even though the Italians were making plans to enter the war from the very outset, they were waiting to see who would come out ahead before committing to a side. In March of 1900, it was still not very clear who that would be. Unfortunately, Italy found out what all of the other belligerents already had. Sometimes, these things go beyond the control of nations. Italy would be swept up in the war by factors that they had never considered. Kitchener's invasion of Mozambique had set off a chain of events that would blindside Italy and take away her choices once again.

No One Watching The Back Door

Many of the Victorian Era had thought that if a large war were to erupt in Europe, then it would have most certainly started in the Balkans. Even Otto Von Bismarck, the crafty arbiter of peace, did not feel that all of his skills were up to containing the Balkans. That was probably why, by 1900, people were scratching their heads and wondering how all of Europe could be at war, except for the Balkans.

While no one truly has an answer for this, it is most likely because the area was already burned out from a series of wars that were fought just prior to 1898. Of course, each nation probably had its own specific reasons, but in general, I believe that was the overriding factor. Nothing else seems to make sense when you consider that the region was filled with small, resource poor nations, who were just freeing themselves from centuries of occupation, and all of them had a list of grievances that they took very personally.

One only need to look at a map of the Balkans to see what the basic problem was. The simple fact is, no matter which map you find, the map will be wrong. This was because the legal borders of the region, the kind of thing map makers usually pay attention to, in no way reflected the reality of who was in control, where, when, and why. During the later half of the 19th century, this also frequently changed.

The main cause for this was the slow death of the Ottoman Empire. During most of the fifty years, leading up to the war, the Turks legally owned the entire region. This was recognized by most nations of Europe, but it began to change, and at the Congress of Berlin, an international treaty redrew the map of Europe. It included several new independent states in the region. The diplomats did not do this arbitrarily. The reality was that these states had already existed for years. These states were not the exception in the region, and in fact, they were the rule.

At the time, Bulgaria was not just one, but two separate nations that were legally Turkish principalities. Kosovo, Montenegro, Macedonia, and a host of smaller regions also ruled themselves and were legally still subjects of the Ottoman Sultan. Areas like Bosnia, now completely cut off from the rest of Turkey, was even occupied by Turkey's main foe in the region, Austria-Hungary. Greece had fought and gained its complete and recognized independence. Both Serbia and Romania were eventually recognized as their own states, and they promptly became kingdoms with established dynasties of their own. There were places, like Albania, that were again legally Turkish soil, but in reality, had no government at all.

The region was also racked with ethnic problems that were little more than a sham, but very important to the people who lived there. It basically broke down along religious lines. When the Turks first arrived, they offered tax breaks to anyone who would convert to Islam. The people

who did were initially seen by their
neighbors as traitors and, after a few
centuries, as foreigners that had never
been anything else. If that was not bad
enough, even the Christians of the region
were divided into two separate and very
antagonistic camps, as both Catholics and
Orthodox competed. All of these people
lived in close proximity to each other,
and, from one village to the next, you
never could tell which group would be
dominate. It was a patchwork quilt
without rhyme or reason.

It is not amazing that the region
eventually became involved in the war.
What is amazing, is that they stayed out
of it for so long. I personally believe that
is testimony to the ferocity of the small
wars they had fought among themselves
in the years leading up to the big show.
Greece had fought Turkey less than a
year before the war. The result was that
Greece conquered the island of Crete.
The Greeks even went so far as to
complain that the European blockade had
nothing to do with the Armenians and
was really there to safeguard the Turkish
fleet from being destroyed by the Greek
navy. There might be some truth to that.

Serbia had fought nearly every single neighbor they had, and multiple times. Serbia was ripe with discontent and expansionist fever, although, in all fairness, they did not start all of the wars. There were enough of them to let everyone get the blame. Serbia had yet to fulfill the borders they sought. I say 'they' because this was a wildly popular idea with the Serbian people, and, in reverse of many nations, their monarchy was not as quick to resort to military adventures, or at least, not quick enough to satisfy their own people.

The only exception to all of the instability in the region seems to have been Romania. While the Romanians did fight some wars in this time period and did gain some territory (mostly at the expense of Bulgaria), the kingdom was relatively stable. A powerful dynasty had established itself on the throne, and, in 1900, King Carol I had been ruling the nation for several decades. Romania had prospered in this time period and were the least likely to enter the larger war. Ironically, Romanian strength is what would become her undoing.

The Serbian Crisis

It was another great irony of the war that the spark that would set off the normally volatile Balkans came from the very place that usually kept it relatively stable. The single biggest point of friction between Nicholas of Russia and Franz Joseph of Austria had always been the Balkans. This was most often because Nicholas considered himself the protector of the region, while these lands were squarely in the Hapsburg backyard. The people who lived there were primarily Slavic and, as Nicholas reasoned, so was he. Of course, Russia did have valid security and economic reasons for their constant meddling in the Balkans, but it would seem that pride far outweighed anything tangible.

Now that the war was going on two years, Russia was starting to experience the first real troubles of waging a prolonged and modern war. None of these reasons had anything to do with the military situation on the front lines. If anything, Russia seemed to be doing quite well. Her armies had stopped the Germans in central Poland and had even managed to grab more Polish territory at the expense of Austria-Hungary. In fact, the seizures of Krakow, Przemysl, and Lemberg were the only large cities to change hands, so far, on any front of the war. Nicholas had good reason to be optimistic.

The problem that Nicholas was unaware of and his generals and advisers were only slowly coming to realize was that the Russian Empire's greatest weaknesses were not military. Before the war, no military planners had considered such factors as social, ethnic, and economic to be of any great significance. None of them had ever thought that the war could possibly go on this long, and, in their defense, there was no precedent for the situation they were dealing with. This war was most definitely an on the job training situation for all involved.

While much is made of the polyglot nature of the Austria-Hungary, the truth is that the multi-ethnic problems were common in most empires of the time, and these were problems that no one had figured out how to deal with in peace, let alone during the rigors of general war. When the war first began, these problems seemed to just completely vanish. It appears as if most people were willing to put aside the squabbles with their neighbors to support the larger state that they happened to be living in. As the war progressed, and the casualty lists only kept getting longer, the ethnic and social problems began to resurface with a vengeance.

To be fair to the Russians, in the past, they had actually tried to act responsibly when it came to dealing with the minorities of their empire. There were several recorded uprisings, strikes, and mob activities during the time periods when their harvests were bad, but they also took actions of a more progressive nature to deal with the matters. The imperial government actually appointed commissions to study the problems behind the strife. If you read their reports, you will find these were not dog and pony shows. They actually made solid recommendations to St. Petersburg. The problem was not with the government per se. The problem was that Nicholas simply ignored the reports.

It is a popular notion to believe that Nicholas was a tyrannical, unsympathetic, and greedy dictator, but this was not really the case. The truth was that, on a personal level, Nicholas was a very warm and caring man. All of the personal writings we have about him support the fact that he was hopelessly devoted to his family and most people found him quite personable. The major flaws that Nicholas seemed to suffer from were two-fold. He had a very outmoded view of society, and while that was certainly not uncommon for the aristocracy of his day, in his case it was coupled with his most serious flaw. Nicholas simply did not know how to run a government and he thought he did. When you find yourself living under this kind of leadership, it really no longer matters what the personal qualities of your leader are. They might as well be tyrannical if they are incompetent.

The Russian Empire was just squeaking by, with their new Czar at the helm, before the war. Now that the conflict was starting to put pressure on the civilian infrastructure, the patience demonstrated by the bureaucracy for civil strife was gone. Nicholas did not seem to grasp this, but many of his ministers did. He might not have listened to them, but they began to put their own plans in action to keep this situation from becoming critical. Naturally, the logical step was to win the war and it was in the Balkans that they saw this possible.

Even when Turkey was nominally allied with Russia, the relationship was shaky at best. The simple fact was that the Young Turk movement was never fully in control of the Ottoman Empire, and the two allies were even shooting at each other on their mutual border. The Turkish military never subscribed to an alliance with Russia, no matter what the Young Turks might have thought, and because of this, the Russian Black Sea fleet was never allowed to pass through the Dardanelles straights. The most powerful naval assets of the Russian Empire had remained bottled up in their inland sea.

The only Russian port of any significance, accessible year-round and home of their most powerful fleet, was Sevastopol. It might as well not even exist as long as the Turks controlled

Constantinople and the Dardanelles. What the Russian General staff understood was that, in order to win the war, they would have to sortie their fleet into the Mediterranean. Once there, the Black Sea Fleet could add their strength to that of the French Navy and it would be more than the British could hope to counter. This would never happen as long as the Turks controlled the straights so, a plan was put in motion to rectify that.

The Russians had been quietly massing an army in the southwestern Ukraine for some time. This had not been missed by German military intelligence, but it was thought to most likely be a strategic reserve. At the worst, it was thought to be nothing more than a simple threat to keep more Austrian troops stationed away from the front in the non-critical region of Transylvania. The Germans could not see that this army had anywhere to really go, and as long as they were not shooting at any one in Poland, the Russians were more than welcome to keep them there.

The main problem the Russians had faced up until the spring of 1900 was that German Intelligence was fundamentally correct. These troops did not have anywhere to go, because the only possible front was the Balkans and the political leadership in that area was firmly committed to remaining on the sidelines of this war. The Balkan nations were still recovering from their last set of little wars, and the various leaders in the regions did not appear too anxious for a rematch and, in particular, a fight that would now include their much larger neighbors to the north. What the Russians knew, and the Germans did not, was that the political leadership in the Balkans were not the only voices that counted.

King Alexander I was only sixteen years old when he decided to dismiss his regents and rule the Kingdom of Serbia by himself. His father, Milan, had voluntarily abdicated a few years earlier and then went in to exile for some time. By 1900, Milan was back and had reconciled most of the differences with his son, but the now twenty-four-year-old boy was still ruling by absolute decree. Alexander was preoccupied with the personal intrigues of his own family, along with his status as a playboy, rather than foreign affairs. After Serbia was soundly defeated by the Bulgarians, Alexander not only seems to have decided to avoid wars, but to ignore them altogether. The current world war was no exception.

This might not have been the wisest choice for Alexander because his kingdom was very typical of the region in that its borders were arbitrary at best. Despite Serbian claims, Montenegro was effectively independent, Kosovo was largely autonomous, Macedonia was completely up for grabs, Bosnia was firmly under the thumb of Austria, and Albania was legally ruled by the Turks though in reality, it was in anarchy. The sad fact was that half of what appeared on the map as Alexander's kingdom was currently occupied by the Bulgarians. You could almost say that Alexander was really little more than the mayor of Belgrade, except that the real mayor might take offense at such a suggestion.

Alexander's military was not happy with the situation and it was only the appointment of his father, Milan, as commander and chief of the armed forces that kept the Serbian military from rebelling. Milan was a competent leader, and he launched many reforms that made him very popular. He had no wish to regain the throne even if he did not exactly see eye to eye with his son. This kept the situation in check and bought Serbia a certain amount of stability. This was not to last, and it was the news of Kitchener's Mozambique expedition that would be the final straw.

Dragutin Dimitrijevic was a young Serbian Captain that, ironically, had a career that very much paralleled that of his king. The two men were born only three days apart, and they both began their public service at the tender young age of sixteen. The similarities ended there, however. Dimitrijevic was quite talented at his job, charismatic, and was very deeply committed to the idea of a greater Serbia. It was something that his monarch seemed to have lost any interest in. Perhaps that was what drove Dimitrijevic into the shadowy world of secret societies and international espionage. We now know that the young Captain was head over heels in both. He had not only joined but also taken over command of a group of radical pro-ethnic Serbs known as the Black Hand. He also became a paid agent of the Russian military.

Unfortunately, we are not completely certain exactly how deeply Dimitrijevic was involved with the Russians. His file, maintained by Russian security services, has survived, but only the folder itself. There is nothing inside it. Whatever was there has long since been removed, but we can surmise that the very existence of the folder proves a connection, and the lack of papers proves that the contents were potentially sensitive. Beyond that, Dimitrijevic's actions and timing speaks volumes about what those papers probably did say.

It was no secret that, from the very start of the war, Dimitrijevic had used his position on the General Staff to agitate for Serbian intervention. He was certainly not alone in that many young Serbian officers saw the war as a chance to "liberate" the Bosnian Serbs from the hands of their Hapsburg oppressors. Milan, as commander in chief, was able to keep a handle on the situation until the double blow came, one from Kitchener and the other from his own son. The violation of neutral territory in Africa was no harder felt anywhere than in the

Balkans where borders were more suggestions than reality. Now that the British had opened that door, moderates such as Milan, could no longer argue that neutrality was their best protection. It now appeared as if staying on the sidelines was only inviting an attack.

Then came the first rumblings of Alexander's latest conquest. It was not the kind of kingly conquest that one wants to see from a mighty ruler. It was Alexander's latest bedroom conquest, one of his mother's hand maidens, and now he wanted to marry her. It had not become public knowledge yet, but Alexander's liaison and intentions were widely known in the inner circles of government. When he announced plans for a national celebration in the summer of 1900, there was not a single official in Belgrade that did not know why. Alexander was planning on making his engagement, to Draga Masin, public.

This was all that Dimitrijevic needed to make his move. Milan was effectively neutralized from stopping the young Captain who had now won over the support of the majority of the junior officers in the army. Alexander was arrested and the only thing that kept him from being executed was his father who still commanded a great deal of respect. Apparently, Dimitrijevic was hoping that Milan would agree to reclaim the throne and lead Serbia in a glorious war of ethnic union.

They reached a curious compromise that left Alexander on the throne, but in prison. His would-be queen, Draga, had also been arrested but she was quickly forgotten about. She would later be released, would never marry, and die in obscurity many years after the war. Milan would remain at his current post, but for all practical purposes he would act as de facto head of state in cooperation with a Prime Minister that Dimitrijevic would later appoint.

Without any official declaration, this effectively put Serbia at war with Austria-Hungary. Franz Joseph was all too aware of the situation in Belgrade and intimately familiar with the personalities involved. This is not to say that there was no declaration. When it came, not two days after Alexander was deposed, it brought about, in Belgrade, all of the fanfare and promises that had been seen in the cities of the major powers almost two years before. This included promises from the Russian ambassador who assured the Serbs that help was on the way.

Fortunately for Franz Joseph, the enemies of Austria Hungary, new and old alike, had many problems. Dimitrijevic and his conspirators had been so busy trying to get their nation in the war that they had barely given any thought as to what they would do once they had accomplished their goals. They promised the cheering crowds, in Belgrade, that they would liberate the oppressed Serbs to the north (translation: they would conquer Bosnia), but not only did they lack any substantial resources they had no plans on how to accomplish this task.

Meanwhile, the Russians had their own problems. There would be many that would plague them during the Balkan campaign, but at the moment their main problem had one name, Romania. Unlike the Serbs, the Russians had carefully thought the matter out, but unfortunately for them, the Romanian situation was far more complicated than they had anticipated. Romania was, for the Russians at least, the key to the entire region, because without the use of their territory, the Russians had no way of launching, let alone sustaining, any military efforts in the Balkan peninsula. Up until the Russians found themselves obligated to support their new ally, Serbia, the Russians had taken Romanian cooperation for granted. That did not happen as they thought it might.

The Balkan Pit

Napoleon Bonaparte had marched huge armies across the continent of Europe and, just from a light glance, those armies appeared to range wherever they chose. This was not entirely true. Armies were limited to seasonal paths that they could safely travel and were so ancient that nobody is even really sure who first started using them. You might ask why, and there are those who even refuse to believe it, but if you map the major battles and marching armies, from one era to another, you find very similar lines begin to take shape. The battles, even naval, tend to all be compressed into small areas that have been fought over, almost continuously, since the dawn of history. There is a very good reason why.

While there is much fanfare made about exceptions to this rule, the reality that military planners deal with is that there is ultimately only one factor that absolutely guarantees a victory on the battlefield, and that rule is to have the numbers on your side. Napoleon is often quoted when speaking to this, "god is on the side with the biggest battalions". The reason why military men take this to heart is because of a vast sea of experience which has taught this hard-won lesson, over and over, for all of human history. If you want a realistic chance of victory, with only small degrees in the outcome being uncertain, then you need a three to one superiority. If you want absolute victory, then you need a ten to one margin.

Getting those kinds of numbers assembled in one place and at one time has really been the art of war for most of human history. What most lay people generally fail to grasp is that it's trickier than it looks. Any group of people need the same basic things in order to survive. When you assemble an army, they not only need the same supplies as any city of the same size, but they need even more, because an army is a city that is on the move and has a specialized job. This is what truly restricted the movements of most armies for most of history.

The timing of military movement had to be when your army could pick up supplies on the march. The areas that your army traveled in had to actually produce the supplies that you needed, and in the quantities required. Hauling supplies back and forth from a supply base was generally slow, dangerous, and it left you with an Achilles Heel that the enemy could often exploit. Most of the time, it was not worth the effort anyway. For most of human history, the technology to supply a field army away from its base of supplies simply didn't exist. Sure, you could round up as many pack animals as you could find, but their ability to transport cargo is limited, and you now have the added problem of feeding your own transports. They have to carry their food along with everything else.

Then came the railroad and along with it, the era known as the railroad wars. For the first time in history, it was possible to transport everything that an army needed, far away from its base of supplies, for as long as was required. The trade off to this capability was that your line of march was well known long before the war and it was nearly impossible to change. In most of Europe, and even in large parts of North America, this dependency on rail tracks had been solved by simply building more lines until an area was saturated with them. If you went so far as to be out of range of one set of tracks, then you would find yourself already close to another.

Despite the proliferation of railroads in the more industrialized areas, there were still entire regions that lacked such advancements. The Balkans was one such area, and while there were railroads in the region, most of what was there was limited in the volume of goods that they could move, and all but the central lines were nominal in their military usefulness. The paths that these main arteries followed were dictated by the rugged terrain which squeezed any movement into some very constricted areas. It also put Romania squarely in the cross hairs and made their hope of remaining neutral, for the entire war, a pipe dream at best.

The crisis in Serbia was ultimately what doomed Romania and her king, Carol I. The only rail lines that ran from Russia to Serbia were those that followed the lower Danube valley, which was to say, the greater part of Romania. More important was the fact that these lines joined the major north/south artery for the region, in Serbia. This particular railroad ran all the way to Constantinople and that was the ultimate destination of the Russian Army. This rail line was also famous and highly romanticized. It was most commonly referred to in the literature of the time as the Oriental Express.

The sudden change of Serbia's status, from neutral to belligerent, left Romania caught dead in the middle. King Carol had more than a few reasons to want to avoid this conflict, and all of them were not only quite sound, but for Carol at least, very personal because he was born Karl Hohenzollern-Sigmaringen, a German prince. While all of the

European monarchs of the time were related in one way or the other, Carol was not only the cousin of Kaiser Wilhelm, but also, close personal friends with the man. Carol had never forgotten his German roots and, as he saw it, his kingdom would not abandon his homeland.

Unfortunately, the King's subjects did not feel this way. France was wildly popular in Romania at the time, and while the Russians were not particularly liked, they were allied to the French. Up until this point, Carol had halfheartedly advocated for joining Germany in war. The Kings Council had staunchly stood their ground and the resulting deadlock had kept the country at peace. Carol seems to have been perfectly happy with this even if he paid much lip service to his homeland. Then the Russian ultimatum arrived, and Romania could no longer sit on the sideline.

The Russians were playing their diplomatic moves in the Balkans both subtle and smart. They had an inside track on the region and were well aware of it. Their ultimatum to Carol was not worded as a threat and, if anything, it sounded like a friendly welcome and invitation. Romania was invited to join the crusade against the Hapsburgs, but if they chose not to, then all they had to do was not impede the moves of the Russian Army. Basically, the Russians were saying they would settle for rights of transit.

Of course, the Russians must have been well aware that no European Monarch could afford to grant such a request. They were probably expecting a declaration of war from Bucharest. That might go a long way towards explaining the confusion with the reply they did get. Romania both declared war on Russia and granted the rights of passage. It was King Carol who wasted no time issuing a declaration of war, but he was not the only voice coming out of Romania. The King's Council sent another telegram, directly to Nicholas, granting his forces full rights of passage. They probably sent the telegram to the wrong person in St. Petersburg, because the Russian Czar was, at best, only vaguely aware of the circumstances surrounding the current Balkan crisis.

The mixed signals not only delayed the Russian Army from moving, but it

had ramifications that went far beyond
Romania or even Serbia. King Carol
might have been very autocratic, but he
was effective none the less. In order to
balance the power plays from his own
Council, he had sought out foreign allies
that were still in the neutral camp. By
1900, there was really only one left of any
consequence and that was Italy.

Since Carol had first ascended to
throne, he had managed to expand his
kingdom in the only direction that he
could. It also happened to be the only
direction that really mattered. The border
with Austria was long but it also sat in the
mountains of Transylvania, and there
were no railroads in that region. There
were lots of ethnic Romanians living
under Hapsburg rule, but this did not
concern Carol greatly, and besides, large
scale military operations in the
Carpathian Mountains were impractical
and beyond Romania's abilities. South of
the Danube river was a different matter,
and this gave Romania access to the sea.
Carol fought several small wars with the
Bulgarians, who were officially still
subjects of the Ottoman Empire, and
acquired a good deal of territory that
neither Bulgarian Principality soon

forgot. A Bulgarian counterattack to retake their lost territory was always a serious threat to Romania.

In order to keep his domestic rivals from using this threat against him, Carol sought a foreign alliance that would keep the Bulgarians in check. Italy, who had strong ties with Germany, seemed the perfect answer. The Italians were more than eager to oblige Carol since they had designs on other weakly controlled territories that belonged to the Ottoman Turks, namely Libya and Albania. Once the larger war began, this mutual defensive agreement was made official and well publicized. Neither Carol nor the Italians ever thought anything would come of it since, at best, it was only posturing to aid them in other plans. The Bulgarians had other ideas.

No sooner had it become clear that Romania was going to enter the war, even if no one could figure out which side it would be on, the Bulgarians quickly understood the ramifications for their dual state. It was very simple for them; the Russians were coming and they wanted Constantinople. There was only one way they could get there, and it was called Bulgaria. The Bulgarians quickly began their mobilization, and this was not missed in Bucharest where another showdown was coming to a head. This was between none other than Carol and his own Council.

Unlike the Serbian Coup, the Romanian Military did not seek to remove their king. They did not see a need, since they had the backing of both the Council and the general population. The military simply stated that they considered the original Constitution of 1866 to be valid and it was very clear on the status of the Romanian Monarchy. It clearly spelled out that Carol was simply a figurehead with no real power. Carol had ignored the constitution for many years and had even went so far as to proclaim it invalid. Nobody had ever said otherwise, but nobody had officially said it was gone either. In the short period of time between the Russian ultimatum and the Bulgarian mobilization, Romania was being effectively governed by two separate factions that simply tried to pretend the other did not exist. Now, they no longer could. The Bulgarians had now forced a decision.

Carol was not stupid. He saw which way the wind was blowing. He could issue edicts all he wanted, but slowly they were all falling on deaf ears. He tried one last measure to regain control of the situation. Since Carol was the driving force behind the defense pact with Italy, he notified Rome of the Bulgarian situation and formally evoked the treaty. The Italians held good on their promise, since they were preparing an invasion of Libya and this appeared to be the perfect pretext. What the Italians did not seem to realize was exactly where their "landing with both feet" policy was putting them.

The defense pact did not have the desired effect that Carol was hoping for either. Before he could even make the Italian reply public, and before he could even tell the Council of his move to handle the Bulgarian threat, Carol was informed that Russian troops were moving across Romanian soil. They were not invading but riding in rail cars and being welcomed as heroes. The Romanian Army was actively aiding them in this move. This must have been the sign to Carol that he lost the power struggle. He promptly fled Romania, and in a few weeks he would be in Vienna where Franz

Joseph would welcome him as if he were some kind of conquering hero.

King Carol I of Romania would soon be no more. Karl Hohenzollern-Sigmaringen would eventually set up shop in the Transylvanian town of Segesvar, the same place where Vlad Tepes had ruled in exile. The town was well inside Austrian territory and Karl's government in exile had the full support of the Hapsburg Dynasty, which was much the same situation as that of Vlad Dracula from four centuries earlier. Karl would never return to Wallachia or Moldavia, and there would eventually be no kingdom there left for him to rule. Eventually, Karl would become King Carol I of the Independent Kingdom of Transylvania, but that was much later. For now, his actions had altered the entire balance of the war, and he had no idea that this was the case.

When the Italians delivered their ultimatum to the Bulgarian principalities, they meticulously avoided any mention of the Ottoman Empire. They also did not bother to mention anything about a formal declaration of war since, officially speaking, no one really recognized the independence of either Bulgaria. Despite this, the Bulgarians considered themselves as sovereign states and, as the Italians had hoped, they declared war on Italy. What the Italians had not realized was that only an hour before, Bulgaria had declared war on both Romania and Russia.

The government in Rome was not even sure what the real situation was for a full seventy-two hours after the flurry of diplomatic activity that had suddenly committed them to a much wider war. They were more than a little bit confused when the Austrians, the CSA, followed by the British, and finally the Germans severed all diplomatic ties and then demanded that Italy back down. By this time, it was not only too late, but Italy was preparing to enter the war on the side that they thought they were about to fight.

The entire collapse of the Balkans did have one major side effect on the career of a certain British General. The fact that Horatio Kitchener was not boarding a ship for home, recalled, and being put out to pasture in a quiet job where he could do little, was a sign of exactly how desperate the situation had just turned for Great Britain. The fact that Kitchener was indirectly responsible for this entire situation was lost in the heat of the moment. Now, Lord Salisbury needed the man, and instead of sending the recall order, Kitchener was suddenly named to the new post of Commander of Forces Middle East.

The new orders for this new command were no longer just to defend the Suez. If the Russian fleet got out of the Black Sea and not only joined the French Navy, but now the Italian as well, then the Royal Navy would be hard pressed to keep the Mediterranean Sea lanes open. It would be likely that Britain would lose control of the Mediterranean entirely, and, if that were the case, then the Suez would not really matter.

Kitchener was told, in no uncertain terms, to use all means at his disposal to keep the Dardanelles in friendly hands. He was no longer restricted to his means, and a theater of war that had been known for at least some degree of civility between belligerents was about to turn nasty. Salisbury had just taken his attack dog off the leash, and the war in this

region of the world would soon be a no
holds barred brawl of desperation.

A Few Acers Of Wheat

The fall out of Kitchener's
Mozambique campaign cannot be
understated. It not only set off the fuse in
the Balkans, but like ripples on a pond, it
kept right on traveling further from its
source. One chain of events only set off
another and it was never harder felt than
in London. Up until spring of 1900, the
British war plan was monumental, but
the goals were relatively simple. Britain
only needed to defend its vital supply lines
and, so far, they had managed. The Boers
were on the defensive in South Africa
meaning that Cape Colony remained in
friendly hands, leaving the supply routes
from India open. The Suez was out of
harms reach and the French had proven
an inability to close down the
Mediterranean. Greenland and Iceland
were now occupied, and this gave the
Royal Navy more success in running the
American blockade of Canada. The
sudden entrance of Italy into the war now

77

began to change the picture in many little ways.

The convoys that passed through the Mediterranean would require more protection. More protection meant the same number of warships doing double duty, and this ultimately meant fewer convoys. The British alternative was to reroute more traffic around the Cape of Good Hope, and that meant more ships having to travel further through seas that were far more dangerous. The end result was that the essential raw materials coming from India were going to be showing up in fewer quantities and that meant higher prices. The most important of these raw materials was food.

Before the conflict, Britain had experienced a massive population explosion, and feeding that population was critical in even the most peaceful of times. Sizable tracks of British land were becoming urban and domestic food production had not been so low in centuries. Now that Argentina was in the war, this meant that another crucial source of wheat and beef was off the market. Of course, Britain now had access to Junkers wheat from Germany and Confederate beef from Texas, but neither could provide the quantities that Britain required.

Great Britain had become very dependent on foodstuffs from Canada in the pre-war era. This was so much the case that White Hall considered the breadbasket of Canada's central plains to be strategically critical. The US blockade had managed to slow down traffic, primarily the export of wheat, but it had come nowhere near stopping it. What the US had managed more success at was stopping war materials from getting in. Again, the US had not brought things to a complete halt, but they did not have to. By 1900, the situation in Canada was becoming critical and the Balkan situation suddenly caused the Salisbury Cabinet to have to make a very hard choice.

So far, Britain had raised a sizable army at home, but unlike the other belligerents, she had not used this army. Most of the troops were still training in camps and waiting for shipment to Canada where they had always been intended. The problem was the US blockade, something that no pre-war plans had taken into account since British plans had never anticipated having to fight a war of this scale. As a result, the large-scale deployment of British troops to North America had only, so far, been a trickle. To move large sized formations would require large fleets to protect them, and this ran two serious risks. The first was that it would weaken the defense of the home islands and quite possibly open the door for a French invasion. The second was that Britain might lose that fleet and, as a result, lose the entire war. The battle of the Yellow Sea had not been any great encouragement.

Now, the Salisbury government had to make a choice. If the Dardanelle Straights fell to the Russians, then Britain could also easily lose the war. The ownership of those straights was directly linked to how well the fighting in Serbia went, and it was a fight that the Austrians were ill prepared for. Most of their best troops were busy keeping the Russians from crossing the mountains of southern Poland and breaking out on the Hungarian plain. The Serbs did not represent a serious and immediate threat to Austria Hungary, but as Russian troops streamed into the region, that would slowly start to change.

Germany had already promised to divert reserves to the region, but the only real reserve left to the allied cause, in Europe at any rate, was in Britain. Salisbury would have to commit the troops that had been promised to Canada and, by doing so, he was possibly writing Canada off as a loss. The British Army of North America and the Canadian Army were holding their own so far, but the weight of the never-ending series of US offensives was taking its toll. The simple math was that British and Canadian losses were far exceeding their ability to replace those losses. The first cracks in the line were already starting to show.

Vancouver had been a sizable base for the Royal Navy before the war. It was considered strategic because, from that location, they could easily challenge US naval moves towards the far east and the all-important China. As the war progressed, Vancouver also became an important secondary port for supplies that the British were shipping in from their base at Pearl Harbor. By the spring of 1900, Vancouver was a shadow of its former self. The US Navy had shown very little mercy in harassing the base, and, by this point, the US Army had finally managed to isolate the city by land. The rail lines were cut, the mountain passes were occupied, and US artillery was routinely falling on the outskirts of the city. It was no secret to anyone, that soon, that same US artillery would be within range of the Royal Navy base, and Vancouver would have little choice but surrender.

On the other side of the country, the war had not become that critical just yet, but it was widely believed that this was only a matter of time. Toronto was not yet cut off and her defenses were largely intact, but the US was steadily pushing Canadian and British forces past the city. The US advance was almost predictable and never measured in more than a few miles a day, but the allies had not managed to stop it in any way. It was only a matter of time before the city of Toronto would be cut off and under siege as well. The really bad part of this was that the US no longer really had to do this in order to neutralize the city. So many people had already fled town that Toronto's industrial base was not even performing at a quarter of its pre-war capacity.

The situation was even worse than that. Raw materials were no longer getting into the city, so Toronto had almost reached a point of not being worth defending. The British army stated as much and were fully prepared to abandon it. The Canadian government would hear nothing of such talk and absolutely demanded that the city be held to the last. This represented a serious turning point in the relations between Great Britain and its former colony.

Canada had officially become an independent nation over three decades before the war. This was largely in name only. While the Canadians were given a great deal of leeway in their internal affairs, foreign policy and strategic concerns were still being controlled in London. The US threat was considered that great and Canadians had a hard time denying it.

Of all the industrialized nations, at the time, Canada probably still had the most wilderness of any. Most Canadians were largely unconcerned with things like foreign policy since they seemed so far away and had very little to do with the lives of the average person. While the US and Great Britain might have been squaring off for war, right on the Canadian border (a border that the majority of the Canadian population lived by) the reality on the ground was that the average person on both sides largely ignored politics and pretended as if the border did not even exist.

The war had changed many such attitudes. The last real war that Canada had fought had been against the same enemy as now, the United States. That war was over eighty years old in 1900, and the only people who lived through it were too old to even remember. At the time of the first war, Canada was almost entirely wilderness and the majority of her population was Quebecois French. Much had changed in the past century, and Canada had never experienced anything like the war they were now in. Their casualties were higher, per capita, than every other industrialized nation. Most of the North American campaign was being fought on her soil. It was forging a Canadian nationality like nothing else ever had.

This was why the heated protests over abandoning Toronto came as something of a shock in London. It also served as a wakeup call for the Salisbury government. They suddenly realized that while they might not be able to follow through with their original plans for Canada, they would have to do something. Britain turned to her North American allies. It was the only card left to play.

The famous philosopher, Voltaire, had once told his French King upon hearing of the loss of Canada, "Do not worry your majesty, all you have lost is a few acres of snow". Lord Salisbury could not be so optimistic. It was not the snow that concerned him but the golden fields of wheat that were now more important than ever. If Britain lost Canada, then she might very well lose the war.

The Reconquista

In North America, before the war, there were many conflicts being waged between the soon-to-be belligerents. The most well-known of these was the arms race that developed during the eighties between the United States and the Confederacy. At the same time, another conflict was being waged, and it is one that almost completely escaped the notice of the press. Despite the fact that it was rarely recorded in the public record, it was probably of far more importance than how many guns could be produced in factories. Fortunately for historians, the bureaucracies kept meticulous records of what was an "arms race" in the very literal sense. After all, how can one manufacture a rifle without the man to build it, hold it, and eventually wield it in battle. This race was one of immigration.

All four major belligerents in North America had spent the last half of the 19th century in a race to see who could coax the greatest number of disenfranchised Europeans to their shores. The United States was the undisputed winner in this race. The allure of America proved to be more than enough to encourage hundreds of thousands of people from any region in Europe that had an unfortunate turn of events. Famine in Ireland, Italy, Austria-Hungry, and Russia drove many while political and ethnic dissatisfaction encouraged much emigration from regions that were relatively well off. The US population exploded more from this migration than from its own birth rate. With the loss of its southeastern states, with its predominate stock of Scotch-Irish, the US was becoming quite a polyglot society. What was even more important was that the US had both the agriculture and industry to provide for this exploding population.

One has to wonder why the Confederacy did not seem to prosper from this old-world migration. No one ever bothered to ask any immigrants why they found the US to be a superior choice, but there are some hints as to why the Confederacy failed to attract immigrants. The main reason seems to be that the Confederacy did not really try. There was some immigration to the Confederacy in the years between 1865 and 1898, but this seems to be largely confined to Irish Catholics. While the records are unclear, the pattern of where they settled (very concentrated and in a few specific cities) seems to suggest that the majority of the immigration was due to the fact that the immigrants already had relatives living in the Confederacy. Most of those families had probably moved there before the American 61.

The city of Savannah, Georgia, is very typical of many Irish enclaves in the Confederacy. Most of the immigrants came to dominate entire neighborhoods, work in the same industries, same professions, and showed little interest in leaving. The numbers that arrived in Savannah would greatly boost its population and productivity, transforming the city into a serious economic rival and as a leading port to Charleston that had so dominated the region up until then. Savannah's Irish heritage would become a permanent point of pride to the city which, to this very day, still celebrates its heritage. Unfortunately for the Confederacy, Savannah was an exception to the rule and its influence would not spread.

The Confederate failure to attract new citizens was only slightly worse than that of Canada. The main reason here seems to be far less of a mystery in that immigration was completely controlled by the British Empire. London was only interested in settling the region to a point, and all of the factors governing the policy were all dictated by strategic concerns. Britain was not interested in what they saw as a flood of malcontents from the continent overrunning one of their possessions. The fact that Canada was no longer, legally speaking, their possession was irrelevant to that point of view. Britain did encourage many from Scotland and Ireland to immigrate to Canada, but kept the numbers very small so that the population would not grow to an unmanageable size.

What goes unnoticed is that Mexico, under the policies of Maximilian, actually came in a very close second to the United States in snapping up the excess masses of Europe. Maximilian had actually begun his policies as soon as he came to the throne, but it was only after the French garrisons were gone and his regime stabilized that the policies began to show some fruition. In truth, Maximilian only wanted to attract European aristocrats to Mexico. By the eighteen eighties, he had met with some limited success here. Maximilian seems to have been completely unaware of the fact that this trickle of nobility was slowly turning into a tidal wave of commoners, mostly Hungarian, Polish, and German.

This migration made late 19th century Mexico a very odd place indeed. It was not very apparent to outsiders, but Mexico was not unlike many nations of that day, in that it was very multi-ethnic in nature and that was before the new Europeans began showing up in noticeable numbers. While it was common (indeed it still is) to refer to Mexicans as "Hispanic", in truth, the term had a very different meaning in Mexico. If a Mexican were to refer to his fellow citizen as a "Hispanic", then he usually meant the person in question had pale skin, was probably descended from Spanish aristocracy, and most likely lived in a big city. That might suggest that the dividing line meant there was one other group, but even that was not true. Rural Mexicans were more likely to refer to themselves by whatever pre-Columbian group they were born to. Outsiders could not even see this, but to Mexicans the differences were vast and important.

From the very day that Mexico became an independent nation, these differences hindered its development in more ways than one. More often than not, the rivalries between the various ethnic groups and the economic classes would cause Mexico to trip over its own feet just as it seemed to be getting ahead. These internal divisions created a power vacuum that was constantly filled by a line of dictators, most of whom could trace their lineage back to the Spanish overlords who ruled by decree from Madrid.

That was not to say that Maximilian was all that different from many who came before him. He was not, and many of the policies set by his government did not flourish because of anything that he did. Quite often they succeeded simply because he was not competent enough to stop more talented subordinates from carrying out plans that he personally opposed. The primary difference here was what Maximilian did not have to worry about and many of his predecessors did.

Maximilian did not have to worry about being ousted in a coup, lined up on a wall, and shot. A Confederate/British army would show up should that happen, and after the Franco-Mexican War, not many wanted to tempt another foreign invasion. This gave Maximilian some breathing room and he used it to ignore men that might otherwise have been political rivals. Fortunately for Max, many of these men turned out to be both competent and rich. Many were willing to invest money in a land that, for the first time since its birth, showed signs of becoming politically stable.

That is not to say that Mexico had reached that point yet. Before the Great War broke out, Mexico was fighting a much smaller civil war of its own. This war was largely an extension of the rivalry between the Confederacy and the US. The conflict pitted Maximilian's primarily European Army, backed by British money and Confederate guns, against an assortment of rebels that ruled large tracks of Chihuahua and Sonora as their own private countries. These rebels were quite often described in British newspapers as 'bandit kingdoms', and while this was definitely propaganda, it was not too far from the truth.

The two most prominent of these 'bandit kings' was a very young teenager, who went by the name of Pancho Villa, and the man who used to be his boss, Ignacio Parra. Both men were noted as thieves and outlaws before the civil war began in earnest. There are those who will dispute these claims and whether or not they are hero or villain, greatly depends on who you ask. What is certain about these men is that, by 1896, Villa had eclipsed Parra in reputation and firepower. Parra would splinter off with his core supporters and later be killed in an ambush near Hermosillo less than a year later.

It is often suggested that Villa set up his former boss, and while this can never be proven, there is some circumstantial evidence that makes one wonder. The man who led the ambush was an ardent Maximilian supporter by the name of Alvaro Obregon Salido. Despite his political allegiances, it was discovered some time after the war that Obregon had more than a few casual dealings with Villa that were of mutual benefit to both men.

No matter what the circumstances of Parra's death, after 1897, it left Villa in firm control of the rebel forces in Northern Mexico. Villa also had a card to play that he wasted no time in doing so. He quickly accepted guns and money from the United States. With brand new support he was able to go over to the offensive and by the outbreak of general hostilities, in 1898, he had managed to effectively shut down any real control that Maximilian had of the countryside of Chihuahua and, to an extent, Sonora. What Villa could not do was take even the smallest cities where Maximilian's garrisons remained strongly entrenched and despite Villa's best efforts were able to be re-supplied.

Such was the state of affairs in Mexico when she entered the war in 1899. By spring of 1900, nothing had really changed. Up until this point, Mexico had been involved in very little fighting, all of which had been contained in the regions of its most northern states. All of it was little more than a continuation of the war that had been going on beforehand. The only real difference was that the United States was more directly involved now and even this did not seem to change the situation.

Mexico's inactivity was becoming less practical. The final straw was the deterioration of the situation on the Canadian front. As Britain began to lean more on the Confederacy to put pressure on the US, the Confederacy began to lean on Maximilian. By this point, the Confederates found themselves hard pressed to launch a major offensive along their 1500-mile-long front. So far, all of them had resulted in little more than long lists of casualties and nothing had been gained in return. The Confederate General Staff was under no illusions about their ability to capture anything vital. They were no longer even sure they could distract the United States from its invasion of Canada. That did not mean they were without a plan though.

The Confederacy looked at its military options and decided on a two-part operation. The goal was to kick the US hard enough to make them blink and give the British some breathing room in Canada. In order to do this, they realized they would have to go after the US in places that were not only vital, but where the Yankees were weak. The first part of the plan would come later, but the second is what we are most interested in here. For this, they turned south towards Mexico City and Emperor Maximilian.

When the Emperor and his generals

were introduced to the Confederate plan, they were not very enthusiastic. Colonel Max Weygand was present at this series of meetings between the Confederate and Mexican militaries. His appraisal of the plan was that it was ludicrous and, strangely enough, Weygand noted that it was not for any military reason. He simply did not believe that Mexico had the resources to sustain the kind of campaign the Confederates were suggesting.

It's not clear if Weygand understood the political realities of Mexico, but his objection to the Confederate war plan seems to suggest that he did. The primary obstacle to fully mobilizing the Mexican nation was not her lack of physical resources. Despite the rampant poverty, the Mexican economy was booming before the war. Even under the strain that was created by the raiding on international shipping, Mexico was still fairly well off. She had plenty of raw materials, manpower, and even a developing industrial base. The problem was getting the various and diverse Mexican classes to cooperate long enough to harness all of that. Weygand seemed to fully understand this problem.

Apparently, Maximilian did as well. He had to find a cause that would appeal to the old Spanish Nobility, the Church, the indigenous pre-Columbian groups, and the newly arrived immigrants. Most of those groups would be just as happy shooting at each other as they would the enemies of nations like the Confederate States and Great Britain. There was very little love for the CSA or UK and they were viewed no differently than the English speaking whites of the US. One has to wonder how Maximilian came up with his plan, but for better or worse, it seems to have worked. Mexico's tacit support for its allies was about to become a holy crusade. When Mexican and Confederate forces invaded New Mexico, Emperor Maximilian I proudly announced, the Reconquista had begun.

The Teddy Bear

If there were ever a single human being that really deserved the title of superhero, then Theodore Roosevelt would probably be one of the leading candidates. No matter if you consider the man villain or hero, there is no denying the volume of experiences and accomplishments that Roosevelt managed to rack up in a single lifetime. Just a quick glance at a list of all that this man did, and how deeply he involved himself in every single endeavor, reads much like a work of fiction. It's hard to imagine how any person could do so much in a single lifetime. There is little doubt that Roosevelt is far from the most tireless individual that has ever lived, but unlike so many others, Roosevelt understood something that Benjamin Franklin once remarked on. "It's not just important to do hard work, other people have to see you doing it."

No one ever accused Roosevelt of modesty, but unlike George Armstrong Custer, Theodore's trumpet did not seem to be so much an act of vanity as it was a well calculated ploy. Like most tasks that Roosevelt committed himself to, he was very effective with his self-promoting, public relations campaign. Unfortunately for his political enemies, Roosevelt was generally competent at any task he undertook and, quite often, showed signs of brilliance at even tasks he was unfamiliar. It would be of my own opinion that Roosevelt's success had less to do with his intelligence and more to do with his almost inhuman drive and work ethic. The man simply never stopped and, more important, he also surrounded himself with people who were talented at things that he was not.

Roosevelt's foes were many and that included men who were, at least on the surface, supposed to be his allies. While no one was brave enough to write down that they were worried about Roosevelt as a potential rival or replacement, even to the point of jealousy, it seems quite clear that this was the case. This was never truer than the case of John Hay, the US Secretary of State. There are many who wrote down that Hay not only disliked Roosevelt, but also considered the man dangerous. Hay and Roosevelt were both Republicans, and Hay's boss, President Root, was even from the same political machine as Roosevelt. These were, allegedly, Roosevelt's friends so one can only suppose what his enemies thought of him.

The main point that everyone, friends and enemies alike, could agree on about Roosevelt was that he was seething with ambition and quite good at managing his agenda. This was the reason that Roosevelt found himself posted in the most backwater theater of the war, the State of New Mexico, and all courtesy of John Hay. The Secretary of State made it clear in his writings, even if he did not say it outright, that Roosevelt could cause him no trouble from the little fort in Tombstone, New Mexico. It would become quickly apparent that Hay, like so many before him, had completely underestimated Roosevelt which some reporters described as, "The bear in the room."

Before Mexico and the United States found themselves at war, Roosevelt was guarding a very quiet border. He and his friend, Leonard Wood, his regimental commander, had used the time to train a cavalry unit composed primarily of reservists and militia. They had turned them into a unit that proved itself just as competent as any regular formation. This seems to be largely due to the skills of both Wood and Roosevelt that complimented each other. Despite being a medical doctor, Wood was a first-rate soldier who was more than familiar with the modern state of military affairs.

Roosevelt was not only a tireless administrator, but he was also very good at recognizing talent and stocking the unit with individuals that were worth their weight in gold.

Despite the inactivity of the front, Roosevelt was still making the newspaper with tales of his eccentric cowboy cavalry. Most of these tales were wild exaggerations, and many of the descriptions of these men were outright fabrications, but at a time when war news was depressing at best, it made good copy. It was so effective as propaganda that men like John Hay and President Root did not even think of trying to squash the stories. Roosevelt had been a celebrity before the war, but as it drug on he became a household name and achieved the status of being famous for no other reason than he was famous.

When the silent Mexican border suddenly became a new front in the war, Roosevelt was more than eager to put his unit into action. He quickly discovered that very little changed with the border. What did change was a reorganization of the US Army Department of New Mexico. The overall commander was replaced more than once, and the senior officers were shuffled around considerably. Roosevelt found the confusion and turmoil that this caused to be intolerable. Like so many of his efforts in the early war, Roosevelt began a campaign of correspondence and, once again, his pen proved itself to be a far more effective weapon than his rifle.

While Roosevelt's actual impact on the eventual command structure in New Mexico can be debated, there is little doubt that it had an effect. Roosevelt tirelessly campaigned for his own candidate to lead his front, and, no matter if you believe he was responsible or not, his man eventually got the job. One might think it strange, even unwise, that Roosevelt backed a virtually unknown junior officer, but it proved to be another case of Roosevelt's uncanny knack at recognizing talent when he saw it. This was how a recently minted Lieutenant Colonel, by the name of John Pershing, suddenly found himself promoted to Brevet Major General and in charge of an entire front.

While this might have been something of a surprise to those who were far removed from New Mexico, the truth was that there were very few military men in the state who were. Even Pershing's previous commanding officers were aware of who was really running the department of New Mexico, and, in fact, there were two of them. Since before the war, Captain Pershing and his unofficial partner in crime, Captain Fredrick Funston, were the "go-to guys" in New Mexico. The strange state of affairs and politics of this state is largely the reason why.

The US aid to Pancho Villa was mostly handled by Funston, who was acting as, much like his counterparts in South Africa, a private citizen with a reserve commission in the US Army. In practical, day to day operations, the truth seems to be that Funston was acting quite openly as a US Army officer. Pershing was officially assigned to the Quartermasters Office in Santa Fe, but, in reality, he was seldom there. Pershing made sure that Villa's weapons made it to Funston, who then made sure those same weapons made it to Mexico. All the while, Pershing also had a secondary task that he was obviously required to handle with subtlety.

At the end of the American War of 61, the state of New Mexico was actually two separate territories within the US. The western half of what was, in 1900, the US State of New Mexico, was the long-forgotten territory of Arizona. The citizens of Arizona had been highly sympathetic to the Confederate States, and, at one point, they even declared themselves a state of the CSA. It took military action to prevent this from becoming a reality. As a result of this incident, the territory was punished right out of existence by the US. In 1900, there was still simmering resentment amongst the citizens in the western half of New Mexico.

John Pershing was tasked with the job of making sure that nothing came of the Arizona rebels. There were not that many of them, and Arizona was so remote as to make them easy to ignore, but US aid to Pancho Villa suddenly made the area a little more important. Not only was the US using the area as a staging ground for arms shipments, but there was some fear that Mexico might return the favor by arming US rebels much like the Yankee Gringos were doing with Villa.

There is no record of any attempt by Maximilian's government to aid the Arizona Secessionist Movement. There is also no known record that the Confederate States paid them any attention either. The CS Navy did have a single report on the matter, and they seemed to believe that Pancho Villa's rebellion made such an operation (supplying Arizonan's with weapons) risky if not impossible. With this knowledge, something that no one at the time could have known, it would seem that Pershing was handed a do-nothing job. It might well have been, but the side effects were very important.

In the process of dealing with the local citizenry, something that his duties made an absolute requirement, Pershing developed intimate knowledge of how the state worked. Also, while Pershing was not the most personable of fellows, he was quite honest and even more important, competent. Pershing quickly developed a reputation of being no nonsense and effective. If the man gave you his word, then something usually happened. He quickly gained the respect of even his enemies, many of whom would become his effective allies during the war. He would also give something back to the man who was always in his corner, Theodore Roosevelt.

The West Wing

At the least, one might label Theodore Roosevelt as an unqualified hawk. That was most certainly true of the young Theodore who had yet to ever see battle. Some have gone so far as to say that he was bloodthirsty, but that seems a bit unfair. Many point to the day that Mexico entered the war and Roosevelt's reaction to it. There is no denial that he was enthused by the fact that his front was now active, but does that really denote an absolute thirst for blood? Roosevelt was far from the only man who greeted the news with enthusiasm.

One has to qualify the conditions that these men found themselves saddled with in the southwestern United States. Up until their front became active, the most pressing issue faced by officers and non-com's alike was a string of absence without leaves. Most of the troops that were stationed on this front were posted within fifty miles of their own homes and the idea of going back to see the wife, sleeping in their own bed, and a home cooked meal was generally enough to eventually temp even the most stalwart soldier. The area also saw a sudden boom in the pool hall and saloon businesses. A lot of that was centered around the town of Tombstone. A good deal of the men who were not showing up for morning formations were usually too drunk to do so. It was a minor problem but an extremely annoying one for men like Roosevelt.

Needless to say, all of this was indicative of serious morale problems for the US Army. Roosevelt was a very studious individual and, in many ways, he shared the exact same concerns as his men. He wrote of these problems and his, sometimes, ingenious solutions. This included leading a forced march of one of his troops to a Tombstone saloon where he paid for the libations out of his own pocket. It gave the men what they wanted and gave Roosevelt control of the situation. Still, as Roosevelt noted in his writings, it was not what the men really wanted, and he so aptly noted in his journal, "Only the sounds of battle will rectify this most unfortunate situation".

It was not as much a want of bloodlust as it might sound. Roosevelt went on to note that it was more a sense of purpose. The generation that Roosevelt grew up in was saturated with the idea that the events of North America had gone horribly wrong and that the very spirit of America had been betrayed by their southern brethren. If the average Confederate citizen had become comfortable with the idea of being citizens of a separate country, many in the United States had not.

Naturally, Roosevelt's generation assumed the mantle that it was their job, if not outright crusade, to fix what was broken. Roosevelt was particularly fixated with this idea and not because of any lofty rhetoric. For him, it was far more personal. His father had been of military age during the American 61, and, since the family was fairly wealthy, the elder Roosevelt had bought his way out of the war. Roosevelt had never made any secret of the fact that he felt an obligation to make up for his father's sins.

If that was not enough for Roosevelt there were other facts that, most likely, weighed heavily on his mind. No one had ever accused Roosevelt, or his family, of being Confederate sympathizers, but there is some evidence that Roosevelt believed people whispered such notions about him. After all, Roosevelt's mother was from Georgia. Both she and his grandmother had thought the secessionist movement was "madness" and relocated to New York just before Georgia left the US. Even so, a good deal of the Bulloch clan did not, and most of them not only stayed but supported their home state with distinction during the last war. Most notable of those was the current CS Secretary of the Navy, James Bulloch.

Roosevelt was also very typical of the generation for a host of other reasons. Before the war, his life had been that of what could only be described as a drifter. A lot of this can be easily pinned on his restless personality and the fact that he could afford to be a drifter, but he was not alone in his wanderings. Personal tragedies, and Roosevelt had known his share, were quite often amplified by the state of world affairs. It is human nature to want for blame and the CSA had become quite a popular distraction from such things.

Such traits could easily be described as harboring a desire for revenge and there is little doubt that this played into the attitudes of the common US citizen of the day. That was not the entire picture and, in particular, with the men doing military service in the state of New Mexico. A soldier's life, especially in garrison, is one of tedium and bland routine. The work is often mind numbing and the one thing that can offset a soldier's woes is a sense of purpose. Once the US and Mexico were at war, there was a notable difference in the attitudes of the soldiers serving along the border. Unfortunately for them, it would take some time before they got their wish to do something. Once again, it would be Roosevelt's pen that was at the heart of this.

Not only had Roosevelt and Wood been agitating their commanders for the opportunity to act, but so had most of the mid-level officers in the department. While a great deal of blame is placed on the Departmental commanders who preceded Pershing, this is really unfair. For starters, they had no orders to take any offensive actions. While militaries generally reward aggressive behavior, in this case, it was actually sensible given the situation.

Northwestern Mexico was largely neutralized as a threat to the United States by the actions of Pancho Villa. While Maximilian's forces did control most of the towns and villages, in Chihuahua and Sonora, Villa's men made re-supply of those garrisons difficult on the best of days. The terrain itself did not lend itself to supporting large scale military operations anyway. These factors combined to make for what was probably one of the quietest fronts of the war.

The other reason for the lack of US activity was not south of the border, but inside New Mexico. The department was starved for supplies. Active US offensives in Ontario, Alberta, and Tennessee were using up supplies at a frightening rate. They far exceeded pre-war estimates by a substantial amount, and whenever those fronts needed more material or men, they were most often stripped from New

Mexico. When Pershing took command in Santa Fe, he might have been shocked and horrified by the state of his logistics had it not been for the fact that he was already well aware of the situation.

Apparently, so was Roosevelt. His writings bare out that he was both annoyed and understood the supply issues. He even seems to have agreed, but was still angered by the lack of supplies anyway. This did not stop him though. This seems to also be true of both Pershing and Wood. While no one has ever proven it, these three men all seemed to have definitive plans once Pershing was holding the reigns. The fact that they moved so quickly indicates that they had been making preparations for active operations since even before Pershing took command.

This is how, in the summer of 1899, Roosevelt managed to lead his regiment in an invasion of Mexico in what was the first offensive operation on his front. It was at best a minor affair, but you would not know this by the number of headlines it generated. As I have noted earlier, George Armstrong Custer kept a contingent of reporters who were

permanently attached to his
headquarters. He had nothing on
Roosevelt who did not have quite as many
reporters following him into battle, but
some of these men more than made up of
for the lack of quantity. Naturally,
Roosevelt's personal friend, Richard
Harding Davis left Bisbee with the First
US Volunteer Cavalry, but he was not the
only noted name that made the journey.

Ambrose Bierce was no stranger to
the battlefield. The man had served in the
first war against the Confederate States,
in the beginning as a private soldier and
then as an officer who received a
battlefield commission after repeated acts
of heroism in both West Virginia and
Tennessee. Bierce had remained in the
army after the war and he even rose to
the rank of a Regular Army Major. While
stationed in San Francisco at the Presidio,
for reasons known only to Bierce, he
resigned his commission and became a
writer. He was successful, and by the time
he was following Roosevelt, Bierce was
one of William Randolph Hearst's inner
circle. Bierce was also one of the few men
who was privy to the information that
Hearst was harboring ambitions to
ascend to the White House. His presence

during Roosevelt's offensive seems to be directly related to this.

This makes Bierce somewhat of an ironic figure. The man was an outspoken critic of President Root. The fact that the New York political machine, of which Root was a prominent member, considered Roosevelt an undesirable was not well known outside of the machine; however, the fact that Roosevelt was a loose cannon was. It is not a great leap to think that Bierce tagged along on this offensive because Hearst believed that it would ultimately fail, and he would have more dirt on Elihu Root, all courtesy of Roosevelt.

Hearst's estimation of Roosevelt's chances of success was not unrealistic and the newspaper magnate did not have the entire picture to base his calculations on. This operation was little more than a raid since the US Army did not have the logistics to support their troops in the area for very long. This may explain the choice of the target, and on the surface the Mexican city of Cananea seems to be a bit more than Roosevelt could chew. This was only on the surface, and if Roosevelt is to be believed, the limited objectives of the operation were fulfilled.

The single largest factor in operating cavalry in the region was the availability of water. What aided the Cananea operation was the fact that Pancho Villa's forces knew where all of the watering holes were, and this allowed the small force of cavalry to concentrate and operate in the area for a temporary period of time. It seems unlikely that Pershing or Roosevelt actually believed that they could take Cananea. Pershing knew his business and fully understood that Roosevelt could not take artillery with him on this operation. The terrain would not permit it and re-supply would be impossible. Even if, by some miracle, Roosevelt could overwhelm the garrison (that had artillery) then Roosevelt would find himself isolated in the region. To put it simply, staying in Mexico was out of the question.

What made Cananea an attractive target was not just the fact that they could find the water to get them there. Cananea was sitting in the middle of a mountainous region that was rich with copper. A Confederate mining conglomerate, backed by British money, was hard at work building up the infrastructure in the region so that they could exploit this find. The war had only sped up the project as the need for copper was currently at a premium.

As Roosevelt and Villa's troops approached the city, the local garrison pulled in its outposts and patrols. Most of the local civilian populace fled for the city as well. Once the US Cavalry deployed outposts on high ground around the city, the rest of the regiment proceeded to destroy any infrastructure they could find. They were largely successful, but it was not what Roosevelt really wanted nor was it what the reporters had come to see. Judging by Roosevelt's writings, it would seem that he was nervous about this and was even tempted by the idea of taking some kind of offensive action against the town proper. Fortunately for him, an action would have likely been a disaster, and the Cananea garrison was under their own pressure to do something about these bandits.

Colonel Max Weygand had been ordered to personally lead a relief column of cavalry to reinforce the garrison, and as the Emperor put it, "Raise the siege of

Cananea." It was hardly a siege as Roosevelt had no real way of shutting the city down. Weygand even noted that it was much easier to reach the city than was normal. Most of Villa's forces, normally deployed to harass military traffic on the roads, were currently all involved in the operations close to Cananea.

The arrival of the Lancers, and the subsequent attempts to disrupt the US operations, finally gave Roosevelt what he had been looking for. A patrol that was led by none other than the brother of Wyatt Earp, Morgan, stumbled over a Lancer patrol along a dried creek bed just northeast of Cananea. Both sides were looking for a place to water their horses and they had both heard the same rumors (apparently from the exact same Apaches who were out hunting) of a low spot in the dry riverbed where water could be found. There was no water, but this did not matter since both sides were spoiling for a fight.

A skirmish broke out and neither side showed much in the way of tactical brilliance. Apparently neither side even thought to take cover and simply stood in the open shooting at each other. Both sides sent out calls for reinforcements, and once again, without any display of tactics every patrol in the area rushed towards the sounds of the guns. It was a confused sort of fight as reinforcements came in from all sides with no logical pattern. An approaching dust cloud could easily be friend or foe.

Both Roosevelt and Weygand eventually arrived and neither commander could get a handle on the situation. It only ended when the sun went down and both sides withdrew, apparently without any orders from their respective commanders. It is fair to say that most of the troopers involved, on both sides, were not even aware their commanders were on the field. The private soldiers simply realized there was nothing to be gained, were low on ammo, had wounded to tend to, and simply did the practical thing and retreated to their base camps.

As was quite common at the time, both sides claimed victory in the "battle of Cananea." The fact that anyone even noticed such a small operation was largely due to Roosevelt, but you have to remember that this 'victory' was only within the confines of the war that was being waged in the media and their ultimate objective was to sell papers. Both Roosevelt and Weygand were more than aware of the real score. The Americans eventually withdrew back to New Mexico and despite Maximilian's bombastic statements on the matter, Weygand was well aware of the fact that his actions had nothing to do with it. The Americans had also managed to set back mining operations in the region for at least the rest of the war. It was not a major strategic concern for the allies, but at the least it would not help.

All of this was minor compared to the more lasting effects of the raid. Roosevelt had managed to spin the operation, and the skirmish at Dry Gulch, into a win. The fight was very romanticized as it was portrayed as two mounted forces charging each other with sabers drawn. That was not a picture anyone had seen in this current war and Roosevelt's reputation was only boosted in the national mindset. This would have major repercussions a year later.

Roosevelt also demonstrated

something else and while it is seldom considered, it seems to be a major factor in his rising stardom. While he did demonstrate a great deal of personal bravery during his raid, this came as a surprise to no one. Roosevelt's bravery had never been questioned, and in fact it was often thought that he had a little too much of that quality. The most important thing that he demonstrated, and it was the quality that had denied Hearst his prize story, was control. Despite great temptation and seething ambition, Roosevelt showed an unexpected pragmatism in his command decisions. He stayed on mission. While it can be effectively argued that this operation was payback for political favors, when John Pershing called on him in 1900 it would not be. When Pershing really needed Roosevelt and called him into action it would be because the Teddy Bear had proven himself a capable and dependable field commander. This would ultimately be what really propelled Roosevelt onto the national stage.

Force Multipliers

By the spring of 1900, the war had been dragging on for almost two years, and many nations were becoming desperate to find a solution to the quagmire they found themselves in. As had been the case during peace, many nations turned to technology to solve their problems. The results of these efforts would be both strange and mixed. Many of these projects had been in the works before the war even started and quite a few more would be born of conflict. The lasting effect of many of these would resonate for the better part of the coming century while others would simply vanish with a whimper. The one thing that is most certainly true of all of these technologies was that those who invented and used them were completely unaware of how to do so. It would be a learning curve of trial and error and the full effectiveness for most of these weapon systems would be far less than their potential.

One man who inadvertently saw the ground floor for many of these new technologies was not an inventor, or an engineer, nor would he even be remembered in history as such. In 1900, he was a young ensign in the navy of

Franz Joseph, the Hapsburg emperor of Austria Hungary. This young naval officer found much of what he saw so unremarkable that he never bothered to mention any of it in his private diary. Strangely enough, he did write about these things, extensively, in letters to his sister. This was a fortunate turn of events since his personal papers have been long since lost and we only have secondhand sources to tell us what was there. On the other hand, his sister saved all of his wartime correspondence and it both survived and has since become public. The story it tells is very interesting.

Strangely enough, Georg Johannes Ritter Von Trapp would be most remembered as a singer and stage performer. Until the family of his older sister, Hede Von Trapp, released his letters, very little was known of Trapp's wartime exploits beyond official reports. Both Johannes and Hede were long since dead by this time. It would seem that Von Trapp's connection to the new technologies, which emerged in this era, began before the war and was indirect at best. Still, this connection would open many doors for the man that went well beyond his station and rank.

Not long before the war, Johannes married a young lady by the name of Agatha Whitehead. Her grandfather had been instrumental in shaping the war before it started. Robert Whitehead was an English engineer that had opened up a business in the city of Rijeka. At the time, it was the center of naval activity for the Austro-Hungarian Navy, and this was a perfect place for Whitehead because his bread and butter was the manufacture of his invention, the self-propelled torpedo. This weapon changed naval warfare in very profound ways, and even during the war the weapon still bore his name. Most naval officers still called the lethal ship killers, "the Whitehead".

Johannes had met Agatha while he was attending the naval academy which was also located in Rijeka. They married shortly after he graduated, and the war began not long after that. Johannes had very little to do with his wife's family business, but the association most certainly did not hurt his career. His first assignment was as a gunnery officer aboard the SMS Maria Theresa. She was an armored cruiser and one of the newest and most advanced ships in the Hapsburg navy. Because of this, Johannes would find himself caught up in any number of events and actions that would resonate for many years to come.

The first place that Johannes found himself was in China. While his nation was at war with Russia and France, at the time they were still not at war with the United States. For this reason, the Theresa was allowed to dock in the US controlled port of Tientsin to assist in the evacuation of civilians from Peking. All of them had been rescued, by the US General Custer, from the clutches of the Kansu Warriors, but many belonged to nations that were now belligerents. The Theresa, along with several Spanish, Italian, and other neutral transports were allowed to remove the refugees as per the deal between Admiral Mahan and the British Minister to Japan.

It was while he was in Tientsin that Johannes came in contact with an American couple by the name of Herbert and Lou Hoover. While Von Trapp never mentioned this, even in his letters, the Hoovers did. They were taken by Trapp's singing abilities which they first heard in a Tientsin hotel that was serving as their residence. A small social group had formed there during the evacuations, and they spent several evenings with Von Trapp as he and a few others demonstrated their musical skills to pass the time.

The SMS Maria Theresa, and Von Trapp, were present at the battle of the Yellow Sea. The Austrian cruiser never fired a single shot during the entire battle. She was tempered by her orders not to fire on US flagged vessels and the bulk of enemy forces were American. Theresa did try and engage some of the Russian vessels in the enemy fleet, but could never find one to shoot at. Apparently, the Americans were well aware of Theresa's orders since they most obviously ignored the vessel. Theresa's bad luck would continue for over a year. She spent most of her time patrolling for both enemy merchants and raiders. She would claim to come very close in locating and engaging a French cruiser force in the Caribbean Sea in early January of 1900. It was later discovered, only after the war, that Austrian Intelligence had been completely wrong and the force was a phantom, a deliberate bit of misinformation planted by the French

'Office of Statistics' in Paris.

A few months later, the SMS Maria Theresa, would finally get her wish and become engaged in an all-out slugfest. It was mid-March and she had been sent south with a small force of allied vessels to eliminate the possible threat posed by the Argentine Navy. This boiled down to one vessel in particular, the ARA Garibaldi. She was a very new heavy cruiser, built in Italy on French based technology, and considered a serious threat to allied merchant shipping in the region. This was a fact that the Argentine government was most certainly aware of since Garibaldi had put to sea the very day that Buenos Aries declared war on Britain. She had orders to proceed to the Ivory coast of Africa where she would join several French cruisers who had been causing serious trouble in the region for some time.

Theresa had been deployed to the area when it became obvious that Argentina was going to declare war. There was a delay of several days before Brazil would enter the conflict, and, technically speaking, even Austria was not at war with Argentina since they had only declared war on Great Britain. Unfortunately for the Garibaldi and her escorts, they were not aware of Maria Theresa's orders. She was to consider a declaration of war on any member of the alliance as a declaration on all. Besides a pair of British gunboats, she was the only vessel in the region that could protect the Falklands.

The Garibaldi, and her escort of three corvettes, had no idea the ship was hostile when Theresa approached and then opened fire at close range. Theresa scored multiple hits on the Argentinean cruiser. The corvettes were obviously as shocked as their cruiser since they were very slow to react. By the time they did, the British gunboats had come out of Theresa's shadow and engaged with torpedoes. It was a very lopsided victory for the allies. One of Garibaldi's escorts was completely destroyed, literally blown out of the water, and another seriously damaged. The other fled without ever firing back.

The Garibaldi was down but not out. She did try and fight back, but the Austrian crew proved to be far better trained and ready. In less than an hour, they had pounded the Argentine's into submission. Garibaldi was suffering from fires that were raging out of control. Her boilers were out of action and her magazines were intentionally flooded in order to prevent the fire from exploding the ship. She had also failed to land a single hit on her attackers. Her captain struck his colors, ordered his crew to abandon ship, and then he requested aid from his attackers to help evacuate the sick and wounded. After his crew was off, he scuttled his vessel at sea and, like the captains of old, he went down with his ship.

SMS Maria Theresa's victory was not widely reported in the press. It seems that the allied leaders were not that interested in reminding their people that the war had expanded to South America. This did not mean that the victory went completely unnoticed, and the SMS Maria Theresa did gain one enthusiastic fan, and he was an important one because he was an Emperor. It was none other than Maximilian I of Mexico. Being a native Austrian, a Hapsburg, and also a former officer in the Austrian Navy it seems only natural that Maximilian would celebrate the victory. He invited Theresa to pay a courtesy call and her officers found themselves in Mexico City where they were wined and dined by the Mexican elite.

It was during the visit of the Theresa's officers that the Confederacy and Mexico were finalizing their plans for the offensive against the United States. There were far more Confederate officers in Mexico City than was normal. One of these recently arrived Confederate Officers was also a Naval Officer even if he had never seen a single day of duty aboard a ship. He was an engineer, an inventor, and a noted eccentric by the name of Lieutenant Commander Astin Greene. At this point, Greene had spent his entire war in either Mobile (the home of the Confederate Navy), Montgomery (the home of the Confederate Steel Industry), or Norfolk (the home of one of many of Greene's pet projects). He was eager to take a trip to Mexico and get out of his usual routine. He was also quite eager to explain and promote his new project that had, ironically, originated in Mexico.

It was during this time that Greene had become aware of Von Trapp. There seems to have been two reasons why, although only one has ever been confirmed for certain. The first and known reason was because of who Von Trapp was married too. The Whitehead Torpedo was instrumental in one of Greene's projects and he snapped at a chance to talk to the boy. The other reason seems to have been a bit more personal, in that, both Greene and Von Trapp shared the friendship of a certain couple, Herbert and Lou Hoover.

Going Greene

Astin Greene could have been almost a stereotype had he so chosen to be. He came from a family of means and at least four generations of inherited wealth. His father, Sheraton Mascot Robert Greene, was a very influential man in his home state of Mississippi. He had political connections that ran deep in both the HP and DCP. The man had a legion of devoted followers as well as a sizable group that hated him just as much. That is quite normal for a man in the elder Greene's position, but in his case, Robert Greene seems to have earned it. This would play greatly in shaping the lives of his eight children, of which Astin was the second to youngest and one of only three boys.

Robert Greene was a veteran of the American 61, and while he did see combat, he never seems to have stood out in any particular way. As far as the official record goes, Robert never achieved any status beyond that of a private soldier. He would later claim the title of colonel, and while he never once directly claimed that this was anything other than ceremonial, he also never went out of his way to say that it was not. Robert himself had come from a large family and at least two of his brothers had fought for the United States. In 1900, his youngest sister, Eliza Greene May, was still living in Chicago and was something of a prominent citizen there. Robert never tried to hide any of this, but like his phantom colonelcy, never advertised the connection either.

All of these family connections would come to play in the shaping of Astin's life. Unlike so many of their neighbors in the Mississippi river valley, the Greene's plantation and lands came through the American 61, largely intact. Although many have speculated that this was due to Greene's traitorous brothers, this does not seem to be the case. There is no direct evidence, but Robert Greene's home seems to have been spared due to his own father's Masonic ties. In either case, when Robert returned from the war, he had a roof to put over his head. That was more than many in the area could boast since large sections of Mississippi had been occupied by the enemy for over two years. This was the source of much of the animosity towards Greene, and when the time came to hand out indemnity payments, it only got worse.

After the war, the United States had been obligated to make several large payments to the Confederacy. They were sizable payments, to compensate their former states for the damage done by the US Army. They were spread out over the better part of almost three decades, and in reality the US never finished paying it before the start of the next war. What amounts they did pay were quite often devalued. Much political hay has been made about several of the pre-war depressions, and there are those who suspect that these were deliberately caused by the US government. There is no direct evidence of this, but it is curious that a great deal of these economic down turns occurred almost in synch with the payment schedule to the CSA. In effect, the inflation was reducing the actual value of the paper currency transfers.

The US also drug its feet when paying, but not for the reasons one might think. Many in the US realized that as long as the payments were going on, the US would have some amount of influence in Confederate politics. They were not wrong. When you look at this situation, you then realize that the damage to the CSA was not only beyond the ability of the US to pay for, but there was probably not enough wealth in all of North America and Europe combined to cover the mess. Now you can begin to see the problem faced by many Confederate politicians.

In defense of the Confederate leadership, you can understand that they had something of a duty to make sure this income was invested in sectors of their infant nation that would ensure its future. Much of the criticism they faced (which must be noted that it came long after this entire affair was said and done with) is true in that the system of payments did become hopelessly corrupt, but in the end it does seem to have been spent wisely even if it was unfair. Some states, such as Arkansas, actually held lotteries to see who would get what and when. This seems to have been the least corrupt method employed, but even so, the system still did not avoid any of the controversy that was seen in other states. Also, Arkansas was proclaimed as having the hardest time of any state in recovering from the war.

The state of Mississippi was not so visible in its methods of distributing the indemnity, and the fact that there was any money at all was not even widely reported in the state. The timetables were kept so tightly guarded that one might think they were a military secret. That is why it is impossible to know exactly how Robert Greene managed to get a sizable sum of the money. There is no doubt he was owed something, but many were angered in the fact that he had started off much better than everyone else. Even the most reasonable of people had to ask why it was that he deserved any of the limited funds that were trickling down when others were living in tents.

Robert Greene's actions explain the situation better than any words written on the matter. He did use the money to improve his own property and businesses, but these were interests that also benefited the entire county he lived in. This did leave him as the undisputed, if unofficial, king of the county, but it also ensured that people had food clothing and shelter at the same time. Despite the fact that he was putting back into the community, many were more angered by Greene's investments than even the fact that he got money that they felt were owed directly to them.

The CSA had fought against change. That was a basic concept that even those who didn't truly understand it, felt on an almost instinctual level. Now that they had won the war, many were angered over the fact that their own leadership were changing the very things that they had fought to preserve. Men like Greene were a symbol of this hate. What a lot of these people failed to grasp was the fact that it was one thing to backseat drive and complain (while they were US citizens), but quite another to actually have to run their own nation without the benefit of blaming their former brethren who now sat north of an international border. Now, if the Confederacy were to survive, then they would have to implement the very changes they had fought against.

This was the environment that Astin Greene grew up in. Judging by his own writings, he seems to have largely ignored it. In that respect, Astin would appear to be quite typical of most engineers in that his attitudes and dealings with his fellow humans were quite simplistic. Astin's mind seems to have always been hopelessly deluged in the world of machines. He was a consummate tinkerer and this fact was not lost on his father. Of course, Robert most definitely wished to separate his children, and by extension the reputation of his family, from the constant political turmoil that had become his life. This is probably why he sent young Astin abroad for his education.

It was common for wealthy Confederates of the time to attend prestigious universities in England. Robert had already educated two sons by this method and was sorely disappointed with the results. It had cost him a great deal and he seemingly got little in return. At Robert's core, he was a businessman, and if not exactly cheap, he did not see that he could keep his fortune by spending money just for the sake of it. His sister, in Chicago, had a suggestion for Astin and this involved a new University in California, called Stanford. She wrote Robert and explained that, if accepted, freshmen did not have to pay tuition. It was more than enough to get Robert to agree.

At the age of 17, in 1891, a somewhat socially inadequate Astin Greene took his first trip to a foreign country. The son of a wealthy Mississippi planter enrolled in a university belonging to his nation's most hated enemy, the United States. While this was not exactly rare, it was not common either. Astin found himself isolated and the attitudes of many on campus were not favorable towards him. This seems to be as much a result of Astin's intelligence as it was his nationality. Astin showed an uncanny disposition towards engineering and would often show up many of his fellow classmates. He never seemed to understand the ill will that it generated.

Astin's oddball status would also ensure that he would find himself in the company of two other social un-desirables. The first was Herbert Hoover. The man had not even attended high school, had been admitted to Stanford when he failed the entrance exams twice, and was working his way through school. His future wife, Lou, was also a student and stood out from everyone else because she was a true minority on campus. She was the only woman there. Lou was not the kind of person to let her gender stand in her way. On more than one occasion, she was noted as acting and even dressing as a man, participating in male activities, and she carried herself with a determination to do something besides find a husband, get married, and have children. In this day and age, it was somewhat scandalous. It was also the reason why she, her future husband Herbert, and Astin all closely bonded.

By 1898, they would find themselves living in two separate nations that were at war with each other. It would weigh heavily on Astin and he seems to have buried himself in his work. Of course, he spent the first year and a half of the war working primarily in Montgomery where the Confederate Steel industry was centered. He had workshops there and was involved in virtually every project that the CSN considered important. Many of his innovations and inventions would wind up on the revolutionary battleship, the CSS Texas. Many would become standard on every new class of vessel. Then, there were the Holland submersibles. While we take Astin's inventions for granted today, they were all something of a surprise to those who actually knew the man personally. Just the fact that he joined the Navy was earth shattering to many.

Freedom From Lines By Lines

Astin had surprised everyone when he returned from the US and almost immediately applied to the CS Naval Academy in Mobile. He would graduate from there at the near top of his class and seems to have found several patrons that singled him out for his talent as an engineer. That was something the

Confederate Navy was always sorely short of and eagerly seeking. This also might go a great deal towards explaining why Astin joined the Navy. In the late 19th century, if you lived in the CSA and wished to work on machines, there was no better place than the CSN. If this was truly the explanation for Astin then he had made the correct choice of career paths.

A light examination of Astin's impact on the war would seem to indicate it was marginal at best. This is particularly true when you consider it in light of future accomplishments, most of which can be traced directly back to his days in the Navy and the Montgomery workshops. All of this is an illusion for two reasons. The first of which is that Astin's innovations were not the kind that are usually written about because they are not very glorious. They don't make headlines because they don't make a story that people usually want to read. The second is because his effect was very subtle. He changed a lot of little things and, it would seem, even he did not understand the implications. This is only natural when you consider that, at his heart, Astin was not a military man.

It would be a report from the Confederate War department that would lead him to Mexico. Several members of the Confederate General staff had been impressed by the Mexican use of the armored cars employed by their cavalry. This was despite the fact that the Mexican Lancers were so disappointed in them that they no longer used them and, in fact, had never wanted them in the first place. There were many who believed that where the Mexicans had failed, the Confederacy could not only make it work, but also improve on it. Strangely enough, Astin was not one of these.

When he was first handed the plans for what was being called a "Land Battleship", he quickly let it be known that the entire design was impractical. The internal combustion engine had been around for nearly a half century at this point. The personal automobile had been around for about twenty years with the invention of a practical carburetor. In 1899, all of these were still the toys of the very rich and few had seen military service. Astin had seen the Mexican designs and he fully understood that Mexico was way ahead of everyone else in the engineering required to make this work. What the Confederate War Department wanted was as Greene wrote, "Silly humbug."

Someone in Richmond, most obviously not an engineer, had dreamed up the idea of not only armoring a car to be proof against small arms, but against artillery as well. They wanted to put more than a Maxim gun on it. They wanted to do as the ANV had around Washington. They wanted to mount artillery on the thing. Greene quickly understood that the design was so heavy that no engine could possibly move it. Even if there were, he had already read about the Mexican experience and it proved what he had suspected.

There were no tires capable of traversing adverse terrain and the military commonly encountered this. The only possible solution was to make solid wheels with metal flanges. This approach had been tried on farm machinery and it had met with mixed success. Military considerations would also, probably, be far more adverse than a farmer's field. It would also make the design even heavier and it was already too much so. For these reasons, Greene scoffed at the project right from the start. He also agreed to take it on.

This is probably where the project benefited from the fact that Greene was no military man. While the generals in Richmond only thought in terms of things that blew other things up, Astin saw the world quite differently. He had showed himself quite adept at understanding mechanical systems, and he obviously saw the military supply system in this light. He knew that what they did have the resources to accomplish, and that would do the most good, was not to put armor on cars, but needed supplies instead. He saw the war department grant as a license to research and build a bigger and stronger engine. He did just that.

When he was finished with an actual vehicle, that went with his new engine, he did not armor the thing. Instead he turned the horseless carriage into a horseless wagon. The truck was not exactly a new design, but Greene's truck was significant in the fact that it was made specifically to survive battlefield conditions. It would not survive a direct attack by enemy weapons, but it was never meant to. What it would survive is the rugged conditions that armies traverse. Many field tests had proven this and, by late 1899, Greene only had one last logistical problem left. It was how to make enough of them, fast enough, to make a difference on the battlefield.

While the automobile might seem to lack any serious advantage over pack animals, this is most certainly not the case. To the modern reader, who is used to having to fill up their tank with gasoline and shell out money they otherwise might not have to, the advantages might not seem clear. To the mind of a late 19th century general, it was even less clear. There were no advantages in speed, since a horse, even a burdened one, could easily outpace a vehicle of that day and age. Fuel for vehicles was both expensive and not so common. At the same time, forage for pack animals was both common and cheap. Most importantly, no matter how rugged you made a vehicle, it could not traverse the terrain that a mule could.

These were all illusions for reasons that were yet to be discovered. You could look at the fact that both pack animals and vehicles both consume fuel. The key difference is that if you do not use your pack animal, he still consumes fuel, and this only serves to increase the amount of fuel required. That fuel takes up precious space and reduces the amount of cargo that can be carried. You also get infinitely more power per any given volume of petrol than you ever could from fodder. This also reduces the space required for fuel.

The speed factor was also highly illusionary. The attitude of the day was greatly shaped by the fact that many had seen a galloping horse outrun the fastest automated buggy. What was not generally recognized was the fact that a horse can't gallop while burdened with supplies nor can he keep it up all day. Animals, like people, get tired and have to be constantly rested. Machinery keeps going until it breaks down and that led to the other most widely accepted attitude of the time. People had seen machines break down almost constantly. Still, when a horse or a mule breaks down, the common practice was to shoot them. Most armies quite often ate the animal after that. If a machine breaks down, more times than not, it can usually be fixed. All of these factors were not so readily evident, but eventually they would prove themselves crucial.

Greene did not seem inclined to debate any of this with his own War Department. He had considerable resistance from Richmond once his plans became apparent. This even prompted a phone call from President Wheeler, but it seems to have had little effect on Greene. He proceeded anyway, and the only thing Mechanics Hall could do about it was to deny him resources. They tried and even that did not work, since Greene was the man sitting at the heart of those very resources. Greene had already produced too much for them, he had a few supporters in Mobile, and it was enough to allow him to continue, but it did force what would prove to be a most crucial change in his approach.

The problem of producing enough trucks, to be of use, had been a problem from the start. Astin's estimates of the Confederate production capacity had been coming up short almost from the start. Now that he had less cooperation and material, he would have to conservatively budget his pet project even

146

more than originally planned. His solution was typical Astin Greene. A man that saw mechanical systems, in everything that he looked at, suddenly got the idea to apply that view to the production system. He quickly realized that it was grossly inefficient, and if it were a design for an engine, he'd throw it off his board almost at once. That was why Greene set about the task of restructuring how things got built.

It was easy enough for him to do it in his own shops where he pretty much had unlimited authority. The production in those shops quickly increased along with the complaints from his civilian work force. Many quit over the reforms, and Greene was often accused of treating his workers as if they were slaves. In the Confederacy, this was no small insult between white men. It did not stop Astin since the war had already disrupted the economy, and for every man that quit, there were ten more who would take their place.

The problem that Astin encountered was with his civilian contractors. His shops could not produce most of what he needed and his reliance on them was high. Many outright refused to implement his innovations. Their complaints were not unrealistic by their way of thinking. At the time, many of even the most menial of tasks were considered skilled labor. In essence, building anything out of steel, even making the metal itself, required an artisan, and these people could not be as arbitrarily replaced as Astin was doing in his workshops. The social stigma that was quickly being attached to Greene's labor force threatened to run off the very men that Confederate industry required to survive. It would put them out of business and bring Confederate industry to a screeching halt.

This is what first sent Astin to Mexico. Emperor Maximillian had already laid the favorable political landscape. Astin's ideas were better received by any number of Mexican industrialists. They began setting up lines of workers and runners, who each did one task. The various parts and supplies were organized right down to where they were stored. It eliminated many time-consuming actions and, more importantly, it suddenly turned a host of jobs that once required skilled labor into something that could be efficiently done by almost anybody and with very little training required.

By early 1900, Astin was getting the finished products required to begin the assembly process for his fleet of trucks. He shocked many of his detractors by how quickly he had managed to produce over a hundred of the vehicles. It gave him enough clout to allow his vehicles to be field tested, but the real question was where?

That was right about the time that the New Mexico campaign began to be planned in earnest, and in Richmond and Mexico City it was quickly realized that one of the single largest impediments to the campaign was the region's lack of water and a need to supply this to the armies. It greatly hampered operations for two reasons. The first was the lack of railroads in the region, which meant that the armies would have to stay even closer to the tracks than was normal. This factor narrowed down the front and eliminated the advantages of surprise.

The second problem was that supply caravans, consisting of pack animals, required water too. Carrying fodder was easy enough, if not bulky, but carrying water was an entirely different matter. Water was both heavier than hay, and no descent water containers that could be strapped on an animal's back existed. There were water sacks and wagons, but sacks leaked profusely and the water wagons could no better traverse rough terrain than an automobile. This all looked to be a logistical factor that could kill the offensive before it even started. Astin's fleet of trucks offered a solution.

Flights Of Fancy

As the Balkan crisis rapidly escalated into another highly contested front of the war, Great Britain found she had little choice but to commit her national army to the continent as opposed to North America where it had always been intended. Even the most zealous of advocates for the defense of Canada, and that included Field Marshall Wolseley, had to bow to the pragmatic concerns that revolved around the fear of a

Russian occupied Constantinople. The Austrians had not only failed to capture Belgrade, but they had now encountered the first Russian troops there. It was clear that the Russians were, once again, surprising everyone with their ability to rapidly deploy their forces.

This was the reason for the Potsdam Conference. Henry Balfour and Garnet Wolseley headed up a small delegation of key British officials who traveled to Germany and met with their counterparts so that they could plan out and coordinate the deployment of British troops on the continent. One of their party was acting in his first official capacity as Second Sealord. He left for Germany on his third day of taking his new job. His name was Admiral John "Jackie" Fisher, and his appointment to the second highest position in the Royal Navy was a signal that change was coming.

The shakeup of the admiralty, caused by the Battle of the Yellow Sea, was still playing itself out. The Salisbury cabinet had become well aware that their navy needed new blood, and Jackie Fisher's star had been on the rise for some time before the war. He was not just a top-notch fleet commander, but the man had worked in nearly every logistical posting the Royal Navy offered. He understood the very inner workings of the organization and had a reputation for not just insisting on change, but understanding what that change should be.

At the start of the war, Fisher had been commanding Royal Navy assets in the Caribbean. This was considered an unimportant posting, since the Confederacy generally handled most of Britain's concerns in this region. It was important to Fisher, who, while working very closely with his Confederate allies, had seen most of the projects they had been working on. This included the construction of the battleship, Texas, and her revolutionary innovations. Unlike many of his counterparts, Fisher did not just scoff at anything that came out of America and he was well aware of the importance of many of the Confederate innovations. He would be instrumental in green lighting Britain's own version of the Texas, the HMS Dreadnaught.

Fisher was recalled to England in

the aftermath of the Yellow Sea. He spent some time working in Plymouth and instituted any number of reforms in the Naval Ordinance Bureau while he was there. It must be noted that while a good number of influential men recognized Fisher's talent, even more seemed to have been fearful of the possibility that he might take their job. The fact was that his career as an admiral, which had spanned ten years in 1900, was one of holding a string of posts that were considered dead end jobs in the Royal Navy. None of these would restrain Fisher or, quite literally in this case, the future that he advocated. The war had now shown that he was right about too many things, and as a result he was finally placed in a job where he could begin to bring these ideas to fruition.

It was while he was in Potsdam that he unexpectedly came in contact with one of these new ideas. Up until now, he had no idea that this project even existed. Fisher and his staff had come to Germany to discuss details of how to transport the army to Germany. He was aided in these discussions by his fellow Royal Navy admiral, Prince Louis Battenberg. Being both German and an officer in the Royal Navy was now helping out Battenberg's career in no small way. He was also able to talk with his German counterparts in their native tongue.

One of these counterparts was none other than Admiral Tirpitz, who was, once again, back in Germany. He discovered from his visiting British allies that he was every bit as popular in England as he was at home. Tirpitz's participation in the Kitchener raid in Mozambique had prompted the British press to write any number of colorful stories about the German admiral, most of which were complete fabrications. No one seemed to care and the British public was devouring any scrap of information they could get about the man. Tirpitz found it all amusing, but little else.

It was during these discussions that both Tirpitz and the other key German Admiral, Otto Von Diederichs, made any number of references to a special project that the Kriegsmarine was working on. These references were completely lost in translation as Battenberg did not seem to even understand what they were talking about in German, let alone being able to translate it into English. It was not helped any by the fact that Tirpitz and

154

Diederichs were constantly bickering with each other. Neither man commanded the other's respect, and they were both highly divided in their opinion of the project in question. Fisher realized that whatever these strange references were, it must be something of importance because of how heated the German debate became.

At some point, Fisher told Battenberg to ask a very direct question about all of these strange references that, up until this point, sounded as if the Germans had figured out how make a railroad engine fly. This question confused Tirpitz because he had been told that the British had been informed of the project. In truth, they had been, but very few in the British military knew about it and even fewer understood it. This all seems to have been due to a clerk at Pall Mall who thought the notification was a joke and tossed it in a bin.

As it turned out, Wolseley knew all about the Zeppelin project, but he had found out by means other than the official notification. He also just assumed that others knew about it, so he never said a word since he equally considered it 'flights of fancy' and unimportant. Fisher seems to have thought his lack of knowledge about this project was largely due to the fact that he was new to his current position. He would later find out that no one in the Royal Navy had any knowledge of it at all. After about two hours of translated explaining, and what could only be described as a game of charades, Fisher finally began to see where the Germans were going with this. It was not the fact that they were using balloons to fly since that was both a common technology and used by most armies for observation. It was the idea of powered flight and Fisher quickly realized its potential. He also had something of his own that he could bring to the table.

What Fisher did not know on that day, mainly because it seems that Tirpitz left the room still believing that the British Admirals knew details that they did not, was the fact that not only had Germany been pursuing this technology, but they had already produced an operational model and were set to go into production if it worked. Fisher would only learn of this when the rest of the world did and by means of the newspapers. He would not have long to wait because, as he sat in the plush Potsdam conference room, LZ-4 was being prepped for her first combat mission over France.

Fisher was still in Potsdam when he learned of this, and he quickly volunteered the knowledge of a secret British project that sounded even more absurd than a flying locomotive. This technology was being informally called the, 'Lightening Detector'. Fisher had connected the dots in the conference room when Battenberg finally figured out how to translate the idea to him. The combination of these technologies could be powerful, and the wheels of Fisher's mind began to turn. Once again, he was right.

Pont Saint Vincent

The act of turning Zeppelin's sky train into a reality did not prove as straight forward as it now seems. The fact that the LZ-4 was the first of his inventions to see front line service says everything about the German's development process. It was the fourth such vehicle they had built and on the day of its first mission, it was the only one that existed. The first three Sky Trains had all been destroyed in the testing process. The number of problems they encountered in turning this into a viable technology were more than Zeppelin had originally thought. The single biggest of these was keeping the vehicle from tipping end over end. The balance problem was both crucial and unexpected.

This is why the LZ-4 was a very curious looking vehicle. It lacked the sleek, aerodynamic, cigar shape that future dirigibles would have. This was mainly due to the railing system that had been mounted on the lower side of the gas bag. It ran from the front gondola to the rear and held a series of weights that could be pulled along the railing from back to front. It was the job of two of the six-man crew, one stationed forward and one aft, to work these weights in flight and keep the vehicle balanced. The entire thing looked much like a giant Chinese abacus and was even informally referred to as such. No one, however, would call it that in front of Zeppelin who grew angered at the suggestion.

Of course, the real miracle was not that the Germans eventually made it work, for the idea was sound enough and most of the technology that went into the completed project had been around and was tried and true. What was amazing was that they had gone from nothing to a workable prototype in less than a year and half. The feverous work and speed of development impressed more than a few influential men in Berlin. This included Tirpitz and most of the German Admiralty who were used to dealing with the schedules for building ships. It could take years to assemble a ship and that included well tested designs. What these airships were proving, more than anything else, was that they could be quickly manufactured and, more important, the resources required to build them were not even a fraction of the cost of a sea-going vessel. The only real question left was, would they actually work?

There had been some feverish debate over what to do with their prototype. The more conservative faction had insisted that it be used for observation only. It could render service and Germany would not risk losing her only prototype. Since the test was going to take place under the command of Alfred von Schlieffen, he got the final say in the matter and he would hear none of that. Schlieffen already had observation balloons and he had not supported the project for that purpose. Schlieffen was tired of doing little more than fending off French assaults on Metz and Strasburg. He wanted to crush France and his idea for the deployment of LZ-4 was an offensive one. He wanted to drop artillery on the enemy's heads.

Schlieffen's staff toyed with any number of targets for their new toy. It took some time for the most informed of his staff to convince their general that the LZ-4 had limitations. After much debate, they finally decided on a target that could give them the most bang for their very limited buck. They decided to go after the French supply lines, and the best way to do that was hit it at a natural choke point. They also had to find one that was within the LZ-4's limited range. That was another concept that seemed to have been well beyond Schlieffen. When he was informed of the matter, he asked a simple but pointed question, "Why can't it fly where I tell it?" Representatives from Zeppelin tried to explain, but Schlieffen grew quickly confused, then turned angry, and gave up as he stomped off back to his office.

This was how the LZ-4 lifted off, ironically, on the morning of April 1st. As you might have noticed the date, it was ironic because it was April Fool's Day. It was just one of many inauspicious beginnings to Germany's new grand Air Navy. The second of these seemingly horrible omens would come at takeoff.

The ground crew had no idea what they should be doing. Many had never even heard of such a thing let alone seen an airship before they were brought out to the field just east of Metz. One man, for reasons known only to himself, held firmly to one of the guidelines even after all of his comrades had let go. The LZ-4 lifted effortlessly into the air. This crewman found himself dangling. The ship's crew only discovered this when they tried to pull in their lines and couldn't budge the one that this soldier was still hanging on to. It would take hours for them to land, and the argument about what to do became academic only fifteen minutes later, when the soldier lost his grasp and fell to his death.

Fortunately for the LZ-4, she flew the first leg of her journey with no more tragic incidents. It was only then, after spotting the city of Nancy, that the crew discovered a certain problem that no one had given much consideration. The problem was one of actually finding their target. It was trivial to pick a target and point to it on a map. It was easy to find such a target by traveling to it on the ground. From the air, the world looked like an entirely different place, and landmarks of the kind that people take for granted when strolling down a road simply don't exist. One has to find an entirely new set of landmarks and be able to recognize them from a vantage point on high.

It was not that the Germans had completely ignored this factor, they had not. The crew of LZ-4 on that morning were all men who had the most experience in flying. The problem was that all of the testing had been conducted over the same areas, with nice large lakes that they had become intimately familiar with and, as such, had long since mastered navigation of. When they were given their mission to bomb a railroad bridge just west of Nancy, in one of its suburbs called Pont Saint Vincent, they did not think it would be particularly difficult to locate such a target. As they found out, they were wrong.

Besides being a major hub in the supply chain of the French Army, Nancy was also the largest French controlled city in the area. As expected, it was easy enough to recognize. The problems began to develop as they flew around over the city and realized that recognizing one of its suburbs was not as simple. Nancy had many, and there were more than a few rail lines that ran through the area. There were also more bridges than the aircrew had realized. Nancy not only sits on a river but has many canals and every one of them had more than a few bridges. The fact that the French Army had thrown up even more temporary bridges over the river since the start of the war did not help matters either.

The one thing that the LZ-4 did have going for it was the French reaction to their flight or, you could actually call it a lack of reaction. The airship spent the better part of the morning flying around over Nancy and its local environs. For the entire time that it was loitering in the area, it does not appear as if a single Frenchman fired at it. In fact, it became quite a wonder and drew many spectators. Civilians were climbing up on their roof tops and searching the skies hoping to see this strange new wonder. Military men were frantically calling their higher headquarters and more than a few panicked. They all knew it was German for there was no way to miss that fact. An iron cross had been painted on LZ-4's canvas and was clearly distinguishable from the ground. Still, reacting to something that was very unknown, and lacking any orders, the French Army did nothing but join their civil populace and watch.

Meanwhile, the crew of LZ-4 were becoming frustrated. Their last attempt to find the bridge involved locating a known landmark, in this case the spiral of a church, and then dead reckoning their way to the target using a map, a compass, and estimated speed. It failed and largely because they had no accurate way to figure out how fast they were going. Their speed would vary greatly and there was little they could do about it. The airship was also getting pushed around by wind currents and would slide and spin. These were minor variations, but it all added up to make accurate navigation impossible.

Finally, LZ-4 gave up on its primary target and looked for anything that might be worth dropping their payload on. They picked the first thing that they saw and was obviously military. Ironically, as it turned out, they were sitting directly over Pont Saint Vincent, but apparently had no idea that this was the case. Why they did not see the bridge at this point is anyone's guess. They chose a target that was located near a set of railroad tracks. It was a temporary depot where the French had just been stopping trains next to an open field and unloading crate after crate of supplies. It was large enough to hit and certainly looked juicy enough for the LZ-4 to expend her four bombs on, that were converted artillery shells for a naval five-inch gun.

The tactical effects of the attack were completely negligible. The bombs lacked any fins or control surfaces to help them drop accurately on the target. They dropped like rocks, but not how anyone had thought they might. They were bottom heavy and were flipping end over end as they fell. Only one shell detonated, and it completely missed the target. This seems to have mostly been due to the inability of the crew to hold their airship steady enough for the bombardier. The shell landed on the opposite side of the railroad tracks from the depot and made a large enough crater to suitably impress the French. It had not directly damaged the tracks, but did manage to weaken its bed. Even this was mostly a cosmetic victory since French engineers had the damage repaired in under a day.

What the attack did do was kill six French soldiers, one of whom was a Lieutenant Colonel and commander of the depot. They had been watching the LZ-4 with as much wonder as everyone else and the bombing caught them off guard. It does not appear as if they even took cover from the falling objects. Their deaths were largely the result of debris thrown up from the explosion and this made the headlines in every newspaper in the world.

It has been often commented that if you want to know how effective your weapon is, ask your enemy. France gave Germany, and particularly Zeppelin, the most effective bomb damage assessment they could ever hope for. It was not because the reports of the LZ-4 raid were accurate, they were anything but. The truth was that the LZ-4 had accomplished little of any military significance. The raid was most obviously a tactical failure. Despite this, the exaggerated French accounts and the general horror that this new weapon generated was all that Zeppelin needed to continue his work. Kaiser Wilhelm was now Zeppelin's most enthusiastic patron and he would make sure that his new air fleet would get the budget it deserved. Zeppelin would put those resources to good use.

Going From Future To Past

While the war was slowly transforming into a technological terror, of the kind that we all take for granted in the modern world, in some places it had devolved into fighting that would look quite familiar to someone from a previous century. This was never truer than on the

Canadian/Alaskan frontier where it could be argued that the war had begun. Despite being the source of the first crisis that led to the conflict, the Alaskan front had received almost no aid or resources once general hostilities were underway. The people who lived in either Russian Alaska or the Canadian Northwest territories had precious little to fight with, but they did so anyway and with a passion that was probably unequaled anywhere else. For these people, who lived in this untamed wilderness, the war had become extremely personal.

If anything, the war looked much like the Anglo-French conflicts in North America, of a century past. There were regular troops stationed in the theater, but they were few and very ill equipped. There was nothing in the region as advanced as a road, let alone a railroad, and large-scale operations were impossible. Such academic military operations as moving and holding land were beyond the abilities of the forces in the region and the lack of military supplies made them incapable of attacking each other. This is why the most common form of warfare became the raid, and it was largely carried out by people who were, at best, questionably under military authority. These people fought as much, if not more, for their own reasons as they did national interests. In fact, as later events would prove, most of these people had as little use for their own respective countries as they did for that of their enemy.

It must be pointed out that the Northwestern Front was not a unique example of the tragedy that played out there. Such things still go on in the modern world and the cause is a simple one, if not very obvious to most, and ironically this is at the very heart of the cause. When two or more sides have a reason to fight and are denied the means to do so, they almost never stop fighting. What happens, more times than not, is that people simply adjust their plans to fit their means. When they are no longer capable of attacking each other's armies, they tend to go after each other's civilians instead. This is exactly what happened during the Anglo-French conflict of a century earlier and it would repeat itself on the Alaskan frontier.

This front would become one of many sensitive issues between Canada and Great Britain. It would lead to a significant change inside of Canada and forever alter the relations between the two peoples, although, this change would pale in comparison to what happened on the other side of the border. Alaska was already a powder keg waiting to explode before the war even began. This was even true before the discovery of gold in the Yukon valley. Once you added the factor of untold riches, it was like lighting a match to that powder keg. When you consider this fact, it is of no great surprise that the first great crisis of the war began here. What is surprising is that it did not start even sooner.

To say that Alaska was a unique place was an understatement. It was both wilderness with its rugged conditions and lack of infrastructure. It was also very cosmopolitan and managed both at the same time. One could easily say that this was where the world ended, because it was here that all of the peoples, migrating both to the east and the west, finally met each other and had nowhere left to go. This was not a metaphor. In Alaska of the late 19th century, it was literally the truth. Much like South Africa, Alaska had become the most unlikely of crossroads with a very diverse population of people, most of whom had great reason to mistrust the other. Once they had a real reason to fight, over the gold, it was only a matter of time before leaders and factions would begin to emerge. Not surprisingly, most of these would run down ethnic lines.

One of the most vigorous policies that Czar Nicholas had pursued, upon the death of his father, was squashing the growing dissent within his empire. Of course, dissent was how Nicholas saw it even if it is quite apparent that his father, Alexander, had understood what it really was, growing pains. Russia was slowly modernizing, and like most states of the time, she was experiencing the social discourse that came with such needed change. Alexander was relatively tolerant of this, because he seems to have understood that if Russia were to compete with the other powers then it needed that change and you could not have one without the other. Nicholas never seems to have linked one issue with the other, and he set about dealing with the social unrest in a more traditional and autocratic way.

The method that Nicholas favored to deal with his dissatisfied subjects was simply to get them as far away from him as was possible. Russia had vast tracks of unsettled lands to the east, but even Siberia did not seem to be far enough for him. He also had that worthless peninsula in the New World, called Alaska, and if sending rabble rousers to another continent had worked for the British, then why should it not work for him too?

This policy was very successful in the beginning, but it also demonstrated how Nicholas paid very little attention to the details of his own edicts. Ultimately, it would cause more problems than it would solve. This was never more apparent than to his secret police. After the discovery of gold in Alaska, the jails became filled with men who went out of their way to get arrested and deported. The policy was suddenly causing crimes, as opposed to deterring them, and Nicholas never seems to have noticed.

One early deportee was a man that would participate in the Earp Raid of 1898. His name was Vladimir Llyich Ulyanov, and both he and his wife, Nadya, were two people who had dedicated their lives to sowing dissent and causing problems for the powers that be. In that respect, he seems to have been very similar to Earp with one distinction. Earp was interested in causing problems for pay, while Ulyanov seemed to just like it for emotional gratification. Eventually these differences would drive these allies (and by some reports even personal friends) apart. It is true that their actual motivations were vague, and this subject is still hotly debated. What is not debated is that these motivations were equally intense for each man.

We can form something of an educated guess in regard to Ulyanov, because unlike with Earp his past is not as murky. He was born to a family that was relatively comfortable in both finances and social standing. He was the most unlikely of dissidents, but a very good case study in the failure of the policies of Nicholas. Ulyanov's older brother was arrested and executed by the Russian secret police. This was obviously the turning point in the life of young Vladimir. He would eventually find himself in St Petersburg where he came to be a prominent member of a dissident group that was one of only many in the

Russian seat of power. It would be here that he met Nadya and it would also be here that they were both eventually arrested and deported.

Deportation sounds very harsh and, to the Victorian world at least, it was an unimaginable atrocity. To the modern reader, it makes one think of death camps with armed guards, barbed wire fences, and little huts that provide no real shelter against an unforgiving artic winter. In fact, this was not the case at all, and if Nadya's writings and letters can be believed, one almost has to wonder what kind of punishment this was. They were not only provided with a home, but two of them on separate occasions. The trip to Alaska took over a year and they would actually live near Irkutsk for most of the time in transit. They were never under guard and the entire exile seems to have been handled via correspondence. They were also obviously comfortable since they spent a great deal of their time writing. As this infers, they also never worked while under sentence. The government was actually paying them a salary to be prisoners.

When the Ulyanov's reached

Alaska, they were settled in near the port of Sitka. Once again, they were given a home and seem to have been free to do as they pleased. This is most obviously the case since Nadya, quite openly, corresponded with her family and often spoke of leaving Alaska for Europe. She did not indicate that this would have been any problem, and the way she wrote it sounds as if it would be quite easy. This was before the war, the Ulyanov's had adequate finances, and the shipping around Alaska was both international and plentiful. In fact, as records indicate, a good number of Russian dissidents did leave. Most of them would wind up in the United States, Canada, and even Mexico.

That much is ironic, because of what happened next, and it should have been a clue to Nicholas that his policy was failing. More people were trying to get into Alaska than those who were trying to leave. The reason was simple and, once again, it was the Yukon gold strike. While Vladimir Ulyanov would later write that his reasons for remaining were because, "The proletariat of the world were coming to me", I have my doubts that this was the real reason he stayed. Both he and Nadya would make not one, but three expeditions to the Yukon gold fields. None of these attempts seem to have been very successful, but in the process, Ulyanov would learn how Alaska worked. He would eventually wind up in Ketchikan and put this knowledge to use.

The fact that he chose to settle in Ketchikan is somewhat of a clue as to his motivations and plans. At the time that he and Nadya moved there, it was a boom town and a treaty port. This is where most of the "temporary workers" from the United States were allowed to officially enter the Russian Empire. The town boasted a naval coaling station, a garrison of Cossacks, a customs house, and while it was not the official capital of Alaska, it might as well have been. It had long since eclipsed Sitka as the real focal point of power and wealth in the colony, and this is most obviously what drew in Ulyanov.

Since the gold rush, Ketchikan had also spawned a thriving industry of saloons, billiard houses, gambling dens, and brothels. Most of these new businesses were owned by Americans. This is where Ulyanov would first meet Wyatt Earp. Vladimir seems to have had only one distraction from his otherwise monolithic purpose in life and this was billiards. Earp owned a billiard hall. It is likely that whatever plans and motivations that these two formed were done so with pool cues in hand. It can also be easily supposed that the real politics of Alaska was going on in the saloons of Ketchikan as opposed to the government buildings of Sitka. It would be in places like this that both Earp and Ulyanov would build the networks that would carry them through the war and beyond.

Interestingly enough, it would be here that both men would also have some contact with another man who would later become their most ferocious nemesis. His name was Seth Bulloch and he was neither Russian nor American. Bulloch was from Canada and his presence in Ketchikan, in the pre-war days, greatly illustrates how disorganized this wilderness was. Not only did you have an influx of Russian dissidents and waves of Americans (most of whom were German, Polish, Hungarian, Italian, and Irish who had only just recently immigrated the US), but there was a fairly sizable community of Canadians who were settling the area. In many ways,

Bulloch was quite typical of this group. Before the gold strike, they were drawn in by the booming logging industry or what remained of the fur trade. Many of them, much like Bulloch, seem to have just been fleeing civilization in general.

Before the gold, no one in the area cared much about where the border was. The Russian authorities did little to curve immigration and, in reality, could not have done much even if they had chosen to. The Russian colonial authorities, in the personage of a private company that was not unlike the one in Mozambique, had enough to deal with in their ongoing war with the Tlingit tribe that had never submitted to Russian rule. In fact, we do know that all three men, Ulyanov, Earp, and Bulloch participated in at least one campaign against the Tlingit. While some suggest that they did so as comrades in arms, we have no information. Ulyanov was the only source of writing on the matter and, after the war, he destroyed his papers on that subject. All we have now are recollections of others that did note their presence, but did not elaborate.

The one thing that all of this demonstrates is why the war took the shape that it did on this front. The mix of personalities, the lack of any real authority, the scarce nature of resources, and finally the fact that all of the key players knew each other was a volatile mix. People in this area did not choose their sides due to anything as trivial as flags. In fact, Jack London would later note an anonymous comment about nationality, and it seems to echo the sentiment of the people in this region. Someone called a certain flag a, "fancy bed sheet". Who said it and about which flag is not the issue. What it tells us is these people were not fighting for king and country, for some far-off emperor, and not even for some vague notion or political ideal. These people would fight each other for themselves and, as a result, they would do so in the most bloodthirsty of ways.

The Empire Strikes Back

With their enemies already on the offensive, Great Britain and her allies began their counterstrikes from late April to early May of 1900. Many of the leaders and organizers would later write of Herculean efforts to get all of their forces moving, and while I do not doubt this, I do reject their almost universal excuse for missing their original start dates. They all complained excessively about the weather. I can't deny that this is often a factor in impeding military operations, but in this case it seems rather unlikely. The more plausible explanation is that the allied grand strategy was mostly a result of reacting to situations that were largely created by their enemies. It is clear that the state of the war had created quite a shake up in the leadership of the allied cause. Many of the men that would be running both the war departments and the field operations would be very new to their posts.

One might think that many of these men had risen from obscurity due to their actions on the field, but this was not always the case. The perfect example of this was Lord Roberts who, up until this point, had been commanding British forces in India. He had been greatly criticized back in England, both in the papers and privately, for his inaction. These criticisms were valid, but in

Roberts' defense he fully believed that a Russian invasion of India was inevitable. Roberts had been the victim of bad intelligence, and it was something of a coup for the Russian Secret Police who seems to have been ultimately responsible for feeding Roberts this information.

Roberts, who had been a very aggressive commander in his earlier days, did not sit entirely still. It is true that he sent precious few reinforcements to South Africa, but at the same time, Roberts was attempting an invasion of French protectorates in Southeast Asia. Again, Roberts was in possession of bad intelligence, and he greatly over estimated French strength, which at the time, even France's allies thought was vast in that region. The truth was that their strength was every bit the illusion as was the Russian army in central Asia. French Indo-China's real defense lay in the rugged terrain and lack of infrastructure. It prevented large scale operations of the type that Roberts was attempting and what ultimately led to him giving up on his grand designs.

Ironically, Roberts attempts at neutralizing the Russians would have probably worked better in the jungles of South East Asia as opposed to the steppes of Kazakhstan. He might have been better served sending the bulk of his forces into Afghanistan and threatening the crucial Russian lifeline to the Pacific, the trans-Siberian Railway. It's understandable why he chose not to do this. The British had invaded Afghanistan twice in the past thirty years and had not done so well. This could possibly explain why Roberts chose to appoint one of his noted explorers of Central Asia, Francis Younghusband, to organize a small expedition. Their objective was to travel north and into Russian territory where they were to begin sabotage of the railroad.

Younghusband was perfect for the job, as he was very familiar with that region, having led many expeditions there for the Royal Geological Society. The railroad seemed to be an exposed nerve for the Russians, and given its length, it was nearly impossible to defend. Younghusband was charged with avoiding any major confrontation with Russian troops while destroying isolated sections of the railroad in hit and run attacks. The least he would do is slow down the traffic on this vital artery, and at best he would force the Russians to deploy more men to guard the vital lifeline.

As Roberts discovered, his worst-case scenario was not worst case at all. Younghusband led just over one hundred handpicked men north and only he knew the route. No one from the Younghusband expedition was ever heard from again. I will not speculate on their fate or go over the many theories about what happened to Younghusband, as it is now the staple of late-night shows devoted to the paranormal. Conspiracy (as well as Yeti and Alien Abduction) theories are plentiful and can be found in other sources. What is safe to say, based on Russian records, is that not one attack against their precious railroad was ever made.

It was the last straw for Balfour who was now in de facto control of the Salisbury Cabinet. A personal friend of Lord Salisbury, Lord George Cruzon, was dispatched to India to replace the current Viceroy, and his first official act was to relieve Roberts and send him home. Here is where Roberts proved the old axiom of one being promoted to their level of greatest incompetence. Not long after he returned home, he was appointed command of the British Continental Expeditionary Force. One might wonder how Roberts was placed in this most crucial posting and many point to politics. The truth seems to be less ominous and dark. Roberts was simply the only man available with any real experience. This speaks more to the size and scope of Britain's deployments to Germany. It had been a very long time since a British field army had been deployed to the continent and the BCEF was quite possibly the largest ever.

Roberts' first job would be to crack the nut that the army of Franz Joseph had, so far, failed to do. It would seem, at first glance, that Roberts was in no hurry to take Belgrade, but I have to say this is an unfair judgment of him since it was clearly not his idea to wait. That fell squarely on the shoulders of Field Marshall Waldersee, who had some grand designs of his own and viewed the British operations in Serbia as subordinate to the real war that he was fighting in Poland and Prussia. Even though there is little doubt that Waldersee's interactions with

Roberts were partly designed to "put the British Field Marshall in his place," it must also be noted that Waldersee's ideas are not without merit. In either case, Roberts had little choice in accepting Waldersee's plans since he had been ordered to do so.

This was why British, German, and Austrian guns would begin pounding away at Entente lines at the very same instant from the Baltic sea to the Danube river. The Germans would attempt a virtually identical plan to the one that had failed them in the first days of the war. Their objective was to isolate and lay siege to the city of Warsaw. This time was different and to Waldersee's sorrow, far more difficult as the Austrians had now been pushed back to the other side of the Carpathian Mountains and could no longer effectively threaten the Russians from the south. The Austrian attempts to force the passes and seize the city of Krakow would prove to be a complete disaster. Even so, and despite large numbers of casualties, the Germans were slowly pushing the Russians back.

Roberts and the BCEF would have no easier a time in successfully concluding the siege of Belgrade. The Serbs fought tenaciously and inflicted heavy losses on the British assaults against their fortifications. The former King of Serbia, Milan, had used his time, and Russian aid, very effectively. The Serbs fought the British to a standstill. By the time that his initial assaults were finished, Roberts discovered that his army was effectively wrecked. This would prove temporary, but it required time for Roberts to reorganize so that he could go back over to the offensive.

This was not to say that the British offensive was a complete failure. It was far from that. Only, at the time, Roberts had no way of knowing this. The man that was well aware of this was Milan. His forces had already been strained by months of siege and a successive wave of Austrian assaults. What the British had managed to do and quite to the unpleasant surprise of Milan was to inflict terrible losses on his army.

The Serbs were simply not prepared for the tenacity of the British, who proved far more capable than the Austrian conscripts that they had faced up until now. Many of the Austrian units were not Austrian at all. Most of their troops were drafted from regions of the empire that had little love for the Hapsburg dynasty and a good number of their soldiers found themselves more sympathetic to the Serbian cause. More than a few would desert and go over to the Serbian side. Even those who remained would fail to press home attacks or take undue risks for a cause that they had been forced to fight for. The British did not suffer from any of these handicaps.

If the BCEF was in bad shape after the assaults on Belgrade, then it is equally true that Milan's army was a complete shamble. The Austrians were not the only ones who had an army that suffered from political turmoil. Many in the Serb trenches were not fully supportive of their current leadership. Despite the respect commanded by Milan, the opposition to the Black Hand was considerable. While this opposition would never fully organize or outright oppose the war, it did not have to. It was enough to create whispered doubts about the reasons for Serbia's involvement and the competence of the junior officer corps as well as their allegiance to the radicals. This sentiment would be enough to keep most Serbs from wholeheartedly supporting the conflict. It would also greatly restrict Milan's military options.

For Serbia, Belgrade was the entire war. If Belgrade fell to the allies, then Serbia would effectively be out of the conflict. Milan was well aware of this, and it is most likely why he elected to keep defending his positions around the capital. He did so when it was very obvious that he could no longer hold them. Roberts' attacks may not have achieved tactical success, but they did not have to. The British had forced Milan to consume precious resources and manpower that he could not hope to replace. In effect, the only real defense he had left was a bluff and he was lucky that it would take time for Roberts to realize this.

It was also not the only effect. Waldersee's plan was working despite the fact that even Waldersee did not seem to realize it. Fortunately for Waldersee, neither did Czar Nicholas. The coordinated allied assaults had achieved an overall effect that was very similar to Roberts' assaults on Belgrade, of which, was almost a microcosm for the entire front.

The larger allied offensive did not achieve its objectives on the battlefield, but what it did do was force the Russians to divert resources from their own operations. It would strain the Russian transportation system and tax their general staff even if it did not break either. Most important of all, the supplies and reinforcements for the Russian drive towards Constantinople was whittled down until the Russian general staff was forced to postpone it. It was the first tiny crack in what, up until that point, had seemed an almost unstoppable Russian war machine.

Lone Stars

The allied offensive in North America would begin five days after the war heated up in Europe. The original date for the attack had been set for the first of April and kept getting postponed for any number of reasons. It is safe to say that by May the 2nd, Colonel Jesse

James was getting apprehensive about setting foot in the United States for the first time in at least fifteen years. Some have wondered why he waited, and given his reputation the speculation is justified even if it is no real mystery. The reason why he did not lead his troops into northeast New Mexico until the very second his orders specified was simply because of who his boss was.

James had given no small amount of grief to many of his past bosses, all of whom were Directors of Public Safety for the state of Texas. He had even caused one or two Confederate presidents to squirm because, like the politicians in Texas, they found out that there was no controlling this would be anti-US crusader. In return, what James would find out the hard way was that his current boss was just as determined as he was, and more importantly, Major General William Jesse "Bill" McDonald was equally as competent at bending other men to his will. This should be surprising because, even if it is not well known, McDonald was at the heart of many of the stereotypes for what has come to be thought of as the Texan Cowboy.

McDonald's reputation is somewhat ironic in that he never actually worked in the cattle industry. For most of his life, he worked as either a military man or as a law enforcement official in one capacity or another. Following the American 61, in the state of Texas, these two professions were more often than not one and the same. Of all the Confederate States, with the exception of Virginia, Texas had what could easily be considered a standing and effective army that was all its own. Texas was far more exposed to danger than was Virginia. It also had a lot more territory to defend and fewer people to do it with.

The situation faced by Texas fell completely on the shoulders of its Department of Public Safety, which managed all military and police affairs, as well as the state prison system. Strangely enough, public records also show that the Texas DPS owned a number of billiard halls, but exactly why and how were never recorded. While Texans gained a reputation for being no nonsense frontiersmen with a can-do attitude, and with a taste for action the truth was somewhat different. The DPS was a good example of exactly how bureaucratic the state of Texas had become. The various sub-agencies of the DPS were so complicated that even now we can barely understand them. It's doubtful that anyone at that time did.

While tales of Bill McDonald tend towards the kind that has him fighting rustlers, desperados, and apache renegades, the truth is that he was more commonly having to combat bureaucrats and politicians over matters of administration. This was true even if McDonald was never actually officially in charge of the DPS. Despite his lack of a title there were very few people of the time who doubted that he was the guy who really ran things. A lot of this seems to be due to the fact that people really believed his reputation as a 'fighting man' and they were afraid of him.

This might go a long way towards explaining exactly why the DPS appeared to be a logistical mess before the war. When the people with the actual jobs were not the people really doing them, and this was true of more cases than just McDonald's, then it makes it very hard to coordinate with them if you are an outsider. There have been those who have suggested that this was deliberate on the part of the Texans, since it was a common attitude that their state was simply allied with the CSA and not an actual member. In truth, the attitude did not reflect the real situation, but such attitudes do breed strange circumstances.

Of course, one can easily say that such independent attitudes bred some very dubious choices within their own military. The Texan military system was so multi-layered, and nonspecific, that the Confederate General Staff had long since given up on dealing with them. There were three types of rangers under this system and what their specific operations were, could change daily. The regiments that were officially called the "rifles" seemed to suggest that these units were infantry. In practice, this seemed to never be the case since clearly ten percent of those regiments started the war as cavalry units. Some of these units even changed multiple times during the war, and quite often even the DPS was not notified that this had happened.

To add to the confusion was the State's reserve system. The state had an official part time reserve called the State

Defense Force. It had a state Militia which in theory was every able-bodied man that owned a firearm (meaning everyone). It also had an official state police force known as the "State Patrol" that was, in theory at least, responsible for law enforcement by aiding local county agencies. All of this was only in theory and the outbreak of hostilities proved it. It became apparent that many men belonged to all three organizations at the same time. Since they could not very well be in three places at once, what normally happened was groups of individuals would meet in each town and draw straws to see who went to which mobilization. Sometimes they would play cards to choose, while at other times there was gun fire involved in the selection process.

It would not appear as if any officer of the state was involved in any of these informal arrangements. There are also no records to indicate exactly how many men wound up reporting for duty and to where. What we do know is that once mobilization was complete, the Texan Army got a new class of military unit and that was the Texas State Patrol Regiment. The law enforcement duties then became the primary function of the official Texas State Militia, and the State Defense Force was grouped into a single infantry regiment and eventually sent to defend Tennessee.

As confusing as all of this sounds, one has to wonder how it even functioned, yet it did. It not only worked, but far better than other more rigid systems used in states like Mississippi and Georgia. The reason it did seems to all be due to one man, Bill McDonald. This is how he wound up commanding Confederate Operations in New Mexico. The general staff in Richmond had wanted to send a Regular Army General Officer, but for obvious reasons it would be impossible for anyone but a Texan to command, so McDonald was made a Brevet Major General of the regular Confederate Army.

This gave McDonald command of all Confederate units in the Far Western Theater of Command and not just those belonging to Texas. At the time, most of the regular army assets in theater were mostly logistical in nature, such as the newly formed First Motorized Supply Battalion, which consisted largely of Astin

Greene's trucks and its support staff. The only line units that McDonald gained control of, that were of any significance at all, were those that belonged to the Confederate State of Sequoia. This state found itself even more exposed than Texas and most of its military was busy guarding the US border. So far, their main saving grace was the fact that the US was preoccupied elsewhere.

That was not to say that Sequoia lacked troops that could participate in the upcoming offensive. The state commander of troops in Sequoia was a Muskogee (Creek) named Emmet Brown Weatherford. While technically speaking, Weatherford was not even in the military and held no rank, he was in effective control of the troops in his sector. Sequoian politics were even more complicated than those of Texas and an explanation of them could fill an entire book all by itself. The state operated much as a miniature Confederacy inside of a larger one, and most decisions were made by committee meetings, and quite often the authority granted any particular leader was situational. Weatherford fell into this category and often compared himself to ancient Roman dictators. It seems to have been a valid comparison.

This was not to say that Weatherford was unqualified for his job. In many respects, he was probably more qualified for a field command than not only McDonald, but almost any officer in the Confederate Army. Weatherford's family held a very long running connection with the British Empire that predated the Confederate States. A distant relative of his, that he was named after, had led the Red Sticks in the Creek Civil War of eighty years prior and fought Andrew Jackson at the battle of Horseshoe Bend. At the tender young age of sixteen, the current Weatherford had attended the British War College at Sandhurst. He also held a commission in the British Army even if he had not served in a very long time.

Weatherford took McDonald's ascension to theater commander with a grain of salt. He did not stand in McDonald's way, but he did not seem to really change the dynamics of the relationship he had already fostered with the Texan. He seems to have viewed any orders from McDonald as requests. Still, Weatherford complied and gave

McDonald no reason for a showdown that Weatherford had to have known he could not win.

Weatherford's main problem here seemed to have been his skin color. The Confederacy's attitudes about such things were bizarre to say the least. It's even doubtful if the people alive, at that time, really understood them. Not only did people of pre-Columbian descent have the full legal rights of any white citizen, they also had their own state that they completely dominated. Despite this seeming advantage, they were never fully trusted or even unofficially allowed to rise to the top rungs of society outside of their own little area. Relations between the whites and "civilized tribes" remained generally good, but that was as far as it went.

The reason for this seems to be nothing more than simple skin color and this is why it became unmanageably complicated. As his portraits clearly show, Weatherford looked like someone that you would think of as a pre-Columbian. At the same time, he had two brothers that served during the war. One was an officer in the State Militia in

Florida and spent most of his time at Jacksonville. His other brother was a Confederate Naval officer and would eventually command a Destroyer. Both of these men did not share Weatherford's ethnic looks.

This was a typical problem in Confederate society that spilled over into their military which was, like any other military, the ultimate instrument of government. As a consequence, they were not only bound to follow the laws, but they took it very seriously. This ultimately was the main reason that Confederate land forces were very state centered. What constituted a "race" in one state could be radically different from others. Who could hold what post, due to race, was a consideration, and there were more than a few who found it legal to be an officer in one state and, at the same time, found it a criminal offense to even serve in the military of another.

It was after the Confederacy won its independence that its component states began tightening their racial laws. One legislature after another turned out what were virtual books of laws on the definitions of race and what that meant.

Ironically, by the time of the war, none of these laws were active and most were completely forgotten about. It was not due to some progressive attitude. The reason was simply because the law makers discovered a horrifying fact that they wished to keep as quiet as possible. By many of these laws, which governed the status of not only blacks, but also reds, browns, and whites as well, a great many people found out they were not the race they thought they were and this included more than a few influential people. By these laws, many people who had black skin were legally white and vice versa. Since no one would stand for this, the various state governments decided that if you couldn't tell what race someone was, then you were too stupid to worry about in the first place. The issue was allegedly, after all, black and white.

Such were the attitudes that Weatherford faced, and he definitely harbored some resentment, but not enough to complicate or betray his cause. He released two regiments from his small reserve to Texas. They consisted of the First Cherokee Infantry and the Ocmulgee Rifles. They were brigaded with the independent battalion under

James that was now flying the nickname, the Confederate Foreign Legion. After that, Weatherford washed his hands of the matter and the entire operation. No more support would be coming from Sequoia.

While the Legion was still designated as a battalion, the Missourians were anything but. In terms of size, the legion not only had the numbers, but the logistical support units to rate the designation of a brigade, or maybe even a small division. It has been suggested that the unit designation was kept because no one wanted to give James a rank any higher than the one he already had. The arrival of the Sequoian units changed the situation, and subsequently James was promoted to Brevet Brigadier General because his men nearly rioted. The majority refused to serve under the command of anyone with a darker skin color than their own. This seems a rather odd attitude when you considered that there were actually seventeen black men serving in the Legion (quite possibly they were the only unit in the Confederate Army who could officially claim this), one of whom was even a Company First Sergeant. It makes one wonder how much

James had to do with the protests.

Roswell

Bill McDonald had very little time to worry about the squabbling within his own command. He had enough trouble with his counterpart, a man that he theoretically commanded in this operation, but who was far less polite about his refusal to accept a subordinate role than was Weatherford. McDonald could not ignore this man like he was in the habit of doing with Weatherford. That was because this man was Field Marshall Miguel Gregorio de la luz Atenogenes Mariom y Tarelo, and he was not only commanding Mexican troops in this operation, but he also happened to be the Commander and Chief of all the Armed Forces of Mexico.

Before any discussion of details could get underway, the exact nature of Mariom's position had to be discussed in detail and the man simply refused to budge on anything. He was sixty-eight years old at this time, and despite his

extensive experience and German
military education, it had been a long
time since the man had served in the field.
He had not been the Emperor's first
choice for command, but this was
Mexico's largest military operation in its
history. Mariom refused to be left out.
Fortunately for McDonald, it would be
Colonel Weygand who came to the rescue.
He suggested, through McDonald's staff,
that they adopt the same attitude with
Mariom that he had. Tell the man "yes"
to whatever he asked for and then just
ignore him. It seemed to have worked.

Beyond the bickering over titles, the
Mexican and Confederate staffs began to
deploy troops along the lines of
McDonald's basic plan that had been
formulated months before in Mexico City.
While their enemy was greatly
outnumbered, he was dug in on ground of
his choosing. He also had decades to
prepare for this and from what little
intelligence that McDonald was getting
about his opposite number, John
Pershing, it appeared as if the man was
competent. Exactly how much was yet to
be seen.

The one thing that Pershing seemed

203

to be even shorter of than McDonald were reserves. Pershing had a large border to defend and precious few men to do it with. He also had many miles of railroad that had been laid by the US Army for the express purpose of defending New Mexico. Normal considerations that usually went with railroads, such as commerce, were subordinate to its military function. As a result, New Mexico was not heavily populated and most of its newer cities were simply extensions of the army posts that were set up to defend the rail depots.

This gave the Allied forces an advantage in that they could easily overwhelm any of the garrisons they faced. The main concern that McDonald had was keeping Pershing from concentrating his forces. If this happened, then the front would likely stagnate as it had everywhere else. The solution that McDonald hit upon was to try and give Pershing more disasters than he could handle. This meant a series of ongoing strikes along the border and near targets that the US could not ignore. Hopefully, this would keep the Yankees spread thin and maybe even keep Pershing questioning the nature of McDonald's moves.

The largest of these diversions would fall to none other than General Jesse James. His operation would also begin some seventy-two hours before the main attack would be launched from around El Paso, where it would advance up the Rio Grande River valley. James was given the objective of striking at the heavily fortified city of Roswell which was located just east of the mountains on the exposed plains.

Besides the city's abundant water supply, Roswell was of little strategic importance. Occupying the city would give you effective control of a small sliver of the of the state, but what good was having it? The region was geographically isolated and thinly populated. The only rail line that ran to the city was a spur from Albuquerque. It was only a single line affair and easily severed (not to mention it followed narrow mountain passes), so it could not be used by the Confederates. No lines ran into the Confederacy from this area. To put it bluntly, once you captured the area, you could do nothing else. It had been suggested to McDonald that a more worthy target would be the rail hub of Las Vegas. McDonald rejected the notion since the geography made the town easy to defend and it was also heavily garrisoned. Besides that, he wanted the Roswell region pacified, since it would be deep on his right flank as he approached Albuquerque.

One has to wonder if McDonald ever believed that James could even capture the city. There was no real reason to think that James could. He did not outnumber its garrison, and besides, James only needed to threaten the city in order to accomplish his mission. The presence of Confederate troops in the area would keep the US Army pinned down and that was all McDonald needed.

What McDonald did not understand was that his subordinate required a great deal more. It is fair to say that a forty-year-old desire for revenge was not James' alone. Just a quick glance at the correspondence of his men will prove that much. They also possessed something more than a zealous desire to get even. James had seen to it. These men knew how to accomplish their goals and events would prove this even if no one in the Confederate hierarchy, including McDonald, seemed to be aware.

As stated earlier, the Legion was ordered to advance seventy-two hours before the main attack fell on the Mesilla Valley. It was reasoned that it would give James enough time to reach his target so that his attack would begin on Roswell around the same time as the other combat operations began. James chose to interpret his orders in such a way that his main attack should start three days earlier instead of just the advance. McDonald's headquarters remained completely unaware of this due to the way that James advanced. Fortunately for the Missourians, the US army was also in the same boat as the commanding General of the Mexican-Confederate Army.

By the time that James' main columns had crossed the border, his advance parties were already within sight of Roswell. By the time his logistics trains caught up, it was already all over with. His troops moved at an ungodly speed because they traveled in column instead of skirmish lines. They could afford to do this because the advanced teams had long since scouted the axis of advance and neutralized enemy observation posts.

That is not to say that the city of Roswell received no warning at all. Several warnings did arrive, but they were very misleading as to the size and composition of the approaching enemy force. Raids across the border were common and there was nothing in these warnings that would indicate this was a movement in force.

The garrison was a little under five thousand in strength and composed mainly of reservist (men who were older than your average draftee, had completed their initial military service and had volunteered to return to duty). Most of the men at this particular garrison were from Nevada. Most had never seen any serious combat. The warning that they were given was even more vague than those received by their officers. Since they were used to alerts that turned out to be nothing, most of them ignored their sergeants and went about their duties as normal.

When a stand-to was called at around three in the morning, many men did not even show up and a good number more asked to go on sick call. The city was still being combed over by military police, officers, and angry sergeants, who were all looking for their missing men when the first attack fell on the sleepy little hamlet. Yet the disaster cannot be completely attributed to the lack of discipline. There was no overall commander in charge of Roswell.

There was a city Military Superintendent, but he did not get along so well with his fellow officers who were the actual commanders of the units stationed there. He also lacked the official orders that gave him authority over them. It was one of those oversights left behind from the parade of departmental commanders that had plagued the area since the start of the war. Pershing's staff had yet to even notice the problem, let alone fix it. The senior officers in Roswell decided everything with a vote, and, in this case, they had no time.

Several civilian ranchers had discovered the main Confederate Force when it was only a few miles from Roswell. They had delivered the first warning that had prompted the stand-to which caused more problems than it solved. Roswell's perimeter defenses were lightly manned, but this was not seen as an immediate problem, since the senior officers assumed that the Confederates were camped out and were not likely to do anything until dawn, if even then. The US officers began making preparations for a protracted siege, something that they had thought might be possible all along.

What is very clear is that no one in Roswell expected a direct assault on the city's fortifications. They certainly did not expect the kind of attack that came. The Missourians had been practicing these tactics for decades and they were quite eager to put them into practice. The first strike did not come as an artillery barrage, an infantry assault, or even a cavalry charge. It almost seemed as if the enemy had magically appeared out of nowhere and then vanished just as quickly into the dark.

Post 7 was an artificial mound that was topped with six Colt 'potato digger' machine guns and a bunker full of ammo. It was surrounded with extensive fields of wire, land mines, and cleared fields of fire that just kept on going forever. It was impregnable to a conventional assault, but the darkness and the attitude of the men stationed there gave it a serious weakness. The wire was not as formidable as it looked. It could stop men trying to run across, but too high to stop someone from crawling under it. That was exactly what the Missourians did.

The first groups of infiltrators managed to crawl right up to the bottom of the hill, at which point they tossed large bundles of dynamite into the firing pits. These bundles were not set off by standard fuses either. They were all wired to electric plungers and set off with the kind of split-second timing that forty years of practice affords. Post 7 never knew what hit them. One toss landed close enough to the entrance to the ammo bunker and the subsequent explosion was channeled right into the firing pits. The primary defense of the eastern line was gone in the blink of an eye. Post 7 was also not the only one hit. Not all of these preliminary attacks were successful, but enough of them were.

The infiltration groups also managed to detect any number of gaps in the US defenses. They were marked so the groups proceeded right into the heart of the enemy. Many of them would ambush confused US stragglers and prevent reinforcements from reaching the crumbling defenses. Others would even be so bold as to pretend to be their enemy and send entire companies of men in the wrong direction. One of these columns of US troops would be directed right into an ambush. Many of the US soldiers would toss down their weapons and try to surrender. The Missourians would not accept.

That was only how it started. US defenses were in complete disarray when James arrived with his main strike force. Other components of the Legion, as well as the Sequoians, were effectively cutting the town off from any possible help. James still had the dark to his advantage, but he did not lead his men in a direct charge. His advanced teams had already scouted the ground and marked it for good cover as well as removing any obstacles. Because of this, the Missourians were able to remain in column formation (and hence moved quicker than could be expected) until they were almost on top of the US line. Only then did they deploy into tactical lines. They still did not charge headlong in. His men moved forward in a series of counter rushes, like playing leapfrog. One group would shoot at enemy concentrations of fire while the other moved.

The most revolutionary aspect of this attack was the use of artillery. James had several batteries of seventy-five-millimeter guns with his force, but he only brought part of one with his strike team. They did not deploy in a concentrated line as was standard doctrine. The crews man handled their pieces forward, not far behind the infantry, and used the ground and darkness to cover their movements. When they saw a clump of enemy fire that appeared to become heavy, they stopped, readied their weapon, and fired directly into it instead of an indirect barrage as was common for the time. They practically ignored any enemy artillery fire which was proving to be completely ineffective anyway. The US guns could never figure out exactly where to fire.

US troops were confused to say the least. To the average soldier in a rifle pit, it appeared as if the enemy was coming from everywhere and all at once. Any time he attempted to shoot, he found himself on the receiving end of punishing fire. Some of it was described by one dazed trooper as nothing less than "a fire breathing dragon". It was enough to convince many troops to run, if they had the option, while others began quickly waiving white flags.

The US forces were never able to recover from their initial shock. James simply would not give them the time. Every time US troops managed to form some kind of line, they found themselves quickly under heavy fire and then suddenly flanked by what appeared to be a superior force. By the time the sun came up, and the main Confederate supply column had reached its forward destination, most of Roswell was already in Confederate hands and James had managed to capture most of its supplies, still intact. He also had over half of its garrison under guard as prisoners. The US troops that managed to get out never came back.

It was certainly a victory for the men of the Confederate Foreign Legion. They had managed to move further and faster than practically any unit had, in any army of this war. They had also managed to do something else that seemed completely impossible. They had taken away an entire city from their enemy, with minimal casualties, and all in the span of less than three hours. It was such a lopsided and miraculous victory that no one at McDonald's headquarters even believed the reports when they first got them. They had thought that James was only just then crossing the border. It would take them over a day to realize what had actually happened.

McDonald should have been celebrating this cheap and easy victory as an omen of things to come. He was actually quite furious with James because taking the city had never truly been one of McDonald's objectives. McDonald saw it as having alerted the enemy that a major offensive was now underway, and the main Mexican-Confederate force would not be ready to strike for at least two more days. McDonald then began changing his plans to fit the new situation. His orders became counter orders and all at the last minute. When the real attack began, this would be telling in many ways and plague allied forces throughout the campaign.

Strangely enough, in Albuquerque, at Pershing's headquarters, the reaction to the news was almost the opposite of McDonalds. The one thing the Confederate General (McDonald) never seemed to consider was that he had already lost strategic surprise. Pershing was already fully aware that a major enemy offensive was coming. He had been making his own preparations for almost as long as McDonald had. Pershing was not sure exactly how much he could do, but he intended to make a good fight of it. He was not so concerned about a border post like Roswell that was, to him at least, expendable. With that said, it is quite ironic that Roswell became so important. Its loss gave Pershing exactly what he needed, and it was the one thing that he had lacked since he took command of the department, all courtesy of Jesse James.

The Belfort Star

Not long after Confederate and Mexican troops began their first serious thrust into Mesilla Valley, something else of monumental importance was coming to fruition nearly a half continent away, in the Chesapeake Bay. Unlike the first major Confederate offensive of the war, since the failed attempt to take Washington DC, this military operation was extremely small in scope and at the time very overlooked. It almost never happened and largely due to a recent political shakeup.

The long running Secretary of the Confederate Navy, James Bulloch, contracted what some believe was a bad case of malaria while visiting his home in Georgia. The man was already seventy-seven years old and suffering from any number of health issues. He passed away in his bed with his family at his side and left the CS Navy in something of a shamble. This was not because he had neglected running his department and, in fact, it was due to the exact opposite reason.

As noted, Bulloch ran the Confederate Navy as if it was his own private fiefdom. The CSN was probably the single most efficient bureaucracy within the Confederate Military. As long as it stayed that way, then the various

Presidents who came and went, unlike Bulloch, were not willing to spend the political clout to remove a man that was not only doing his job well, but was also doing a job considered nearly impossible to begin with. Bulloch entrenched himself in his position and by the start of the war, there was no one really even qualified to do his job. Bulloch had made sure of it.

This was not to say that there was a lack of men who quickly stepped up and demanded the position, despite how unappealing it must have looked. The fact was that Bulloch had made many enemies over the years, and ironically most of them came from the political party he belonged to. The main source of this animosity was, without a doubt, what some critics of the CSN had scornfully and sarcastically dubbed, "the Great Black Fleet". Even Bulloch had personally disliked the idea, but he and Longstreet had instituted the policy of using former slaves as sailors because the advantages were too great to ignore. At the time, it seemed as if it was the only way to get a very inward-looking nation to take the steps required to ensure its prosperity and security.

The critics of the plan, chief amongst them being former President Wade Hampton, had vowed to end the policy of using blacks as military men. It is a testimony to the absolute power and political skill of Bulloch that Hampton was unable to stop it. Still, the faction that wanted white men to replace the black sailors did not go away, even if they realized Bulloch would have to go before this ever happened. Now Bulloch was gone, and the fact that their nation was in the middle of a war did not seem to bother the men who wanted to instantly replace nearly every sailor in their fleet.

This left President Wheeler in a very uncomfortable position. He also found the battle over the Navy to be quite distracting from things that he saw as important. Having been a general, Wheeler was quite accustomed to just giving orders and expecting others to follow. He expected whoever replaced Bulloch to do just that and Wheeler had no intentions of shaking up his navy at a time like this. Unfortunately, politics in a working democracy are closer to an anarchy, which is the exact opposite of any functioning military structure of the kind that Wheeler was accustomed to.

Until this time, Wheeler had not been faced with a situation quite like the political firestorm that erupted over the death of Bulloch. Wheeler had inherited a government that, despite its quirks, functioned rather smoothly. This seems to have been for no other reason than its own irrelevancy. Once the first war with the United States was over with, the CS Government diminished in importance with every passing year. The fact was the presence of the United States was the only thing that gave the Confederate national government any authority at all. When people felt threatened, they demanded that it act. When they felt safe, they completely ignored it. With the outset of hostilities, Wheeler suddenly found himself dealing with a situation that no other President had since Jefferson Davis.

This situation might have erupted years earlier since the CSN was really the only asset of any importance that the national government had absolute authority over. Bulloch's presence guaranteed stability here, and in many ways it made him even more powerful than any sitting president. Now the entire department was being dumped in

Wheeler's lap, and he was horrified to learn that the only man who knew every aspect of it was dead.

With the exception of the battleship Texas, which was set for sea trials in early summer, and expected to be operational a month or so later, Bulloch's death also endangered any number of projects that were on the boards. They were all at various stages of development, and a good number of them were being supervised by Astin Greene.

Of course, Greene was completely ignorant of the political situation, but many of his benefactors were not. Greene was recalled from New Mexico where he was completely engrossed in the task of figuring out the most efficient ways of using his trucks. He was not very happy about having to report to Mobile, but he did it. The fact was that Greene could afford to ignore presidents, but not the Admirals in Mobile because they were ones shielding him from the politicians.

The Confederate Admiralty was fully aware of the political problem and realized that the current vacuum would not hold. Since they had no idea of who would replace Bulloch, they chose to press ahead with as many projects as they could, while they could. They chose one particular project to press upon Greene, and demand he personally supervise. The reasons for this were unclear to Greene, but he also did not have the full picture and his bosses did. So, after only a mild protest, Greene proceeded to Norfolk, Virginia, where this project was being readied for its first real test.

It was something of a lucky break for the CSN that Greene was in charge of this project in name only. While it is true that he developed many of its systems, he was not the driving force behind it. The man that was really running the show was an Irish immigrant by the name of John Phillip Holland. Ironically, Holland had not immigrated directly from Ireland. He had actually come from New Jersey where he had lived for a short time after leaving Europe.

Holland once stated that what had sent him to America, and had sparked his fascination with naval warfare, were the warships of the American 61. Strangely enough, given his current project, the ships that really captured his imagination

were the CSS Virginia and the USS
Monitor who had unsuccessfully dueled
each other to a standstill. Even as
Holland's first real prototype was being
lowered in the water, he seems to have
been completely unaware of the fact that
it was the CSN that managed to launch
the first successful submarine attack in
history. The CSS Hunley, that made this
attack, was that vessel.

In 1900, the Hunley was officially
still listed as being on active duty even if
she was also listed as missing in action. It
was more a memorial to the submarine,
since there was no one who really
expected it to ever surface again. Still, the
CSS Holland II was officially the second
submarine on active duty at the time.
While the Hunley was still sitting
somewhere, rusting, on the bottom of
Charleston bay, there were those who
questioned if it were not more seaworthy
than Holland's creation. The new
Confederate sub was not entirely finished
when it was ordered into action, and it
had met with many of the same problems
as its predecessor. That was namely
finding a crew, because most sailors
simply refused to get in it. The Hunley
had gotten around this by recruiting a

crew from the Army. Fortunately, they did not have to do it this time.

Compared to the Hunley, the Holland II was an almost space-aged vessel in terms of technology. The Hunley's power source was human muscle and it required a large crew to turn the crankshaft that propelled the boat. The Holland not only had a mechanical power plant, but it had something that very few other warships at the time could boast. She was powered by a small gasoline engine. Her fuel store was quite small, and her range was rather limited, but gasoline is a much superior fuel to coal, and a steam plant would never have worked on a submersible anyway. The main effect of the power plant was that it reduced the size of the needed crew to only three men. This ultimately eliminated the problem of recruiting sailors.

Of course, the needed support for the Holland II was considerable, and it made her value as a military asset questionable. There was an entire dock and warehouse in Norfolk that was required to maintain and launch the vessel. A small army of engineers were required to practically rebuild her after every single cruise. Much headway had been made in fixing these problems, but there was simply no precedent to work with here. The Confederate engineers were having to come up with solutions from scratch. Fortunately, this is where Astin Greene was the strongest, and it is easy to surmise that without his input the Confederacy was liable to never make the Holland work.

Fortunately for the CSN, they were not the only ones encountering unforeseen problems. The very reason why Holland was no longer living in New Jersey, Thomas Alva Edison, was still there and working on his own version of a submarine. By the time of the war, Edison was already a famous inventor, and since the outset of hostilities, he had concentrated mostly on government contracts and weapons development. Ironically, none of these efforts would ever pan out, and Edison's most lasting contribution to the conflict would be something that he had invented, but for which he had never considered its military potential or political ramifications.

Edison's attempts at making his own submersible seem to be completely centered around his obsession with beating Holland to the punch. Edison had gone out of his way to make things difficult for Holland and, combined with substantial cash offers from the Confederacy, wound up depriving the United States of a valuable mind. Edison also lacked the input of Greene. Even if Greene was not the most military minded of fellows, he had a far better grasp of the needs of warships than did Edison. Edison's attempts showed this in everything from his choice of weaponry to workspace for the crew. That might not have been the entire reason that the US Navy eventually rejected Edison's submarine, but it could not have helped.

Greene had spared the Confederate effort a great many of the pitfalls encountered by the Edison. The first and most notable of these was the choice of weaponry. It was clear that Edison had stolen Holland's initial idea of a pair of dynamite guns that were mounted forward and aft on the original designs. Greene quickly saw them as worthless even if there were some similar weapons in service with the Army at the time.

Greene was reasoning that the ultimate naval ordinance had already been invented, so why not use that?

This ultimate weapon was, of course, the Whitehead Torpedo. It had most certainly revolutionized naval warfare, but much like the machine gun on land, its actual effects had yet to be fully realized. No one had taken countermeasures into effect for either weapon, even if they were already being used. A Whitehead could sink any ship afloat, but first you had to hit the target. As soon as torpedo boats were invented, ships designed to kill those torpedo boats, the naval destroyer, were put to sea as fast as possible. The resulting stalemate meant that the true value of the torpedo was not really its use, but simply its presence. This made the Whitehead more of a defensive weapon, and it was something that most Admirals were yet to admit.

What Greene had in mind, if it worked, would change this maritime stalemate. He was banking on using the one real advantage of a submersible, stealth, to deliver a deadly Whitehead before anyone even knew what hit them.

The plan was sound enough, but the real trick was making it work. When the Holland II was lowered in the water, she had no real intrinsic weaponry. In that respect, she was no different than the Hunley. She could only ram a target if she wished to do damage and, much like the Hunley, this would most likely result in the Holland's destruction as well. What she did have, strapped to her hull, was a Whitehead Torpedo, and its bulky addition to the Holland's mass was not so much an afterthought as it was the fact that the weapon was nearly as large as the ship firing it.

The torpedo did not have the bulk of the sub, but it was a good foot and a half longer. It was an almost comical looking thing mounted on pods that were bolted to Holland's port side hull. The weapon could not even be carried in this fashion while the boat was out of the water. Extra straps had to be cut by support personnel after the sub was wet. A very awkward, electrical, and quite impromptu firing mechanism had been rigged up to launch her. Nobody had even given much thought on how to aim it since her crew was praying that it would detach once the torpedo's motor was started.

The Holland was also less than stealthy. She had to be towed to her patrol station by a pair of river boats from the James River Flotilla. It was slow going and the Holland was not the most maneuverable of vessels. Unlike what we think of submarines today, she did not completely submerge ever. She also did not ever truly surface. The ballast on the vessel was not adjustable and she always sat with her conning tower and top deck just out of the water. In practical terms, her constant depth meant that the number of channels that could be taken, in such a shallow body or water, were limited at best. Given the proliferation of mines in the Chesapeake, it is a miracle that all three vessels even reached their destination.

The Holland also had considerable drag. A ship sitting on top of the water, particularly shallow draft vessels such as the patrol boats, were not as subject to the force of tides and currents as was the Holland. The submarine was taking the full brunt of the water and her escorts were constantly having to adjust their course and overwork their engines to keep from being pulled into a bad situation. Again, it was a miracle that the Holland was sitting on station by dark.

After the patrol ships pulled in the tow cables, and then retreated to a safe inlet to wait out the night, the Holland's troubles only got worse. Her engine was not really capable of getting her anywhere, and if she ever needed speed she was doomed. What they were really for was keeping her on station and they were proving to be remarkably inefficient at that. The tide was currently going out and the Holland was expending a great amount of her limited fuel to keep from going out with it. At the rate of consumption, the crew really doubted their ability to remain on station all night. Then, luck happened their way.

The Belfort Star was a short ranged shallow draft steamer that operated out of Baltimore. Since the war had shut down all commerce along her normal routes, the only work that Belfort had acquired since the onset of hostilities was that which the US Army ordered. Belfort had been requisitioned by the Army and sailed under her command for almost two years now. On this night in mid-April, she

230

was making a rather typical journey to the Maryland shoreline to unload over eight hundred US soldiers that were fresh off the train from New Jersey. The men on board were right out of basic training and had yet to even be assigned to a unit. None of them ever knew what hit them. None of them would ever live to see the sun rise.

By Other Means

In the book that is often considered the final arbiter on military matters, "On War" by Carl Von Clausewitz, he is often quoted that war is an extenuation of politics by other means. Many of his students, men who knew him personally, were still on the battlefield and in the war rooms during this conflict. One has to speculate if they still believed him. As the war was closing in on its second anniversary, was it still a continuation of politics? Had it ever really been? Many of the tensions and hot spots that were responsible for the war had long since been made irrelevant at this point, while new issues had risen to take their place.

It would be a far more recent English historian who pointed out the basic fallacy in Clausewitz's theory. Politics, religion, and war are seemingly inseparable, but they are also not cause and effect. The reason they seem so intertwined is because they are all effects of something larger. They are all expressions of culture. If this is the case, then it is easy to see why no one had bothered to attempt to negotiate a cease fire at this point. Did the politicians and generals really believe that there was anything to gain by continuing the fighting? It does not seem to be the case. What does seem to be true is that if the war was an extenuation of politics, then the politics were an extenuation of pride, by other means.

This was never more clearly demonstrated than in the United States. This is not to suggest that it was unique to America, only more visible. The year of 1900 was more than just the last year of the 19th century. It was more than just another year of the war. It also happened to be an election year in a working democracy. Elihu Root was standing for reelection, and it was very clear that the ballot box was quickly becoming a referendum on the war itself. Here we have a clear-cut case of the exact opposite of the conventional wisdom. Here we have politics being the extenuation of the war and not vice versa, as Clausewitz would have us believe.

Root's dilemma was becoming very similar to that of the first Lincoln Administration. His popularity was entirely dependent on the performance of his military. Root was also discovering that spinning stories could only get you so far, and that was particularly true when the single largest newspaper magnate in the country was hinting at his own candidacy. William Randolph Hearst was also holding a potential presidential bid over Root's head like it was a sword of Damocles.

This is not to say that anyone gave Hearst a realistic chance of winning. Even Hearst himself was pessimistic about his chances, and this could explain why he did not actually toss his hat in the ring. For Hearst, his chance of moving in the executive mansion was irrelevant. What Hearst did have the power to do was cost Elihu Root the election, and it was a fact that did not require Hearst to actively seek the office. One has to also consider that Hearst was, more than likely, not trying to throw the election for Root, but court political currency instead. The reason seems simple enough in that Hearst was even less enthusiastic about Root's chief rival winning than was Root.

There were several men running for president in 1900, but from late spring to early summer, the numbers were shaping up and it had become clear that only one man was a serious rival to replace Root. This man was named Eugene Debbs, and his campaigning was based almost entirely on one thing. Debbs was promising to declare a cease fire as his very first act as commander chief. People had the perception of a very clear-cut choice in the matter between Debbs and Root, even if the reality of the situation was entirely different.

It seems rather unlikely that Debbs could have ever followed through on his only real campaign promise. Despite appearances, the majority of US Presidents have simply lacked the power to rule by edict, and this was exactly what Debbs was proposing. Congress would have never gone along with it and neither would have a sizable majority of the population, both of whom were very hard to ignore. There was also the little problem with the enemies of the US who were also unlikely to have been receptive to such a proposal. If they chose to fight on, then anything that Debbs wanted was rendered moot since, at that point, the US could only continue fighting or surrender.

This is all reasoning with the clarity of hindsight. In 1900, it seemed to many as if Debbs' peace campaign was anything but the pipe dream that it truly was. There was great dissension in the US and all of it revolved around the war, but not so much centered on the question of ending it. Most people were angered at its prosecution, and here is where Hearst found his strongest allies. They were not strong enough to unseat Root, but they were enough to split the vote and put Debbs in the executive mansion. It was causing serious turmoil inside the Root administration, and many, including John Hay, were already making plans for how to carry on once they were handed their hat.

These concerns were only minor in

comparison to the tremors being felt at The Sedan and in St. Petersburg. President Boulanger might have been an autocratic dictator, but at least he did have enough of a background to understand how democracies worked. He should have known better, but Boulanger did not trust democracy, and his current position should have been more than enough evidence of that. At the same time, Czar Nicholas not only mistrusted democracy, but he did not even grasp the subtle complexities that came with such a form of government. That is easy to surmise since it is clear that Nicholas barely understood his own government.

What did seem clear to the American partners in the Triple Entente, even if it was not really true, was that the US was wavering in her commitments. They both howled about Debbs and demanded that Root take action. Both Boulanger and Nicholas were less than subtle in suggesting that the American President declare a state of emergency and suspend the election until after the war. The autocrats saw this as reasonable while the American public was outraged. British and Confederate propaganda made sure they were reminded of this at every instance. Root's chances for reelection sunk even lower, and where a skillful politician might have seen this as an opportunity to ring more out of his allies, for Root it was nothing less than an affront to his honor. He sank even deeper into depression. This hurt his chances even more and it became a vicious cycle that was feeding on itself.

The real coup de grace came on the heels of the sinking of the Belfort Star. It is with great irony that this particular thing would cause so much outrage, since, militarily speaking, it was a minor affair at best and insignificant in the grand scheme of things. The losing of just over eight hundred lives was, in comparison to the losses at the front, not even a metaphorical drop in the bucket. Still, this was an election year and the Belfort Star made good copy because of the elements of the story.

Belfort had gone down with all hands and in an instant. This kind of thing is not just death but a frightening one. There was no warning or defense. One minute everything was fine, and the next there was oblivion. It is a frightening prospect to any sane person. Also, most of the men on her were not really men. At least, they were not when you looked through the prism of William Randolph Hearst. These were all just young boys who were fresh from training and had yet to see war. Deep in the subconscious of most people (helped by a famous sketch of their tender young faces, courtesy of Fredrick Remington), this felt like innocence. Last, they never reached the front. So, in one sinking you had horror, the squashing of innocence, and waste all rolled into one neat package that Hearst quickly recognized.

The irony of this situation is that no one in the United States, at that time, even knew what had really sank the Belfort Star. There were no surviving witnesses from the vessel itself, but the shore batteries that covered her route and the escorting gunboat which was trailing about a mile behind her did. Their descriptions of the explosions led the army to conclude that it had been a mine placed in her path. Their official report, turned over to congress almost a year after the incident, would say as much.

The loss of the Belfort might not have had the impact that it did had it not come on the heels of what was universally being called, in the US anyway, the Roswell Incident. Where Belfort spread horror, Roswell was fanning the flames of fear. An American city had been seized and occupied by an enemy force that had done so with great ease. After this, Jesse James became a household name in the United States, where he was even better known than in the Confederacy. Greatly exaggerated tales of the occupation of Roswell only served to fan the flames.

Roswell could have possibly been a boon for Root had it not been for the fact that, just west of the city, where Pershing's forces were opposing those of the Confederate and Mexican armies, the US was in what was seemingly a headlong retreat. This looked very bad to the average reader of the morning paper, but as history would prove, it was most definitely a case of explaining military realities to those who were not on the spot. The apparent collapse of the front was also a deliberate bit of misinformation. This was mostly the responsibility of three men, all of whom had conspired to do so.

Fortunately, for those three men,

this was not the main battle that concerned Root the most. His job was to get reelected and the prognosis of this campaign, being waged with as much aggression and viciousness as any military action, was even worse than that of the New Mexican Front. It was just when Root thought that things could not get worse when they actually did. The Belfort Star claimed her final casualty, and it was none other than Root's own Vice President, Philander Knox.

Knox was not an insider in the Root administration. He was a constant source of embarrassment and one that Root never lifted a finger to help. In fact, whenever Knox caused a scandal, or said the wrong thing, it is clear that Root and Hay let these stories play out in the press by fading into the shadows and not uttering a single word. One might think that this was foolishness on the part of Root, but in fact it would seem this was exactly the Vice President's real job, even if he was unaware.

To put it bluntly, and this is a bit of speculation, it would seem that Root only kept Knox around so that he would have a fall guy when he needed one. From all we know of Knox, he was a competent administrator, a thoughtful man, and somewhat sincere in his dealings with others (at least for a politician). It is hard to show these qualities when someone else is constantly setting you up, and while there is no direct proof of this, it would seem to be the case here. It is the only thing that can explain the actions of the Vice President following the Belfort Star.

When it became clear that a head was required to roll for the Belfort Star in the middle of a hotly contested presidential campaign, from out of nowhere the Vice President resigned. The letter that Knox presented to Root did nothing to truly explain the reasons for his resignation. He vaguely hinted at health reasons, but his subsequent life would dispel this notion even if it was the most commonly accepted one at the time. What had really happened was that Knox had been sacrificed to the altar of public opinion and, ultimately, not just for the Belfort Star, but rather the entire war so far.

While this served to relieve some of the pressure that had been pushing down on Root, it created an entirely new problem that he, and more specifically John Hay, had not counted on. They had already handpicked two possible successors for Knox. Their first choice was a man named Thomas Platt, who was a party power broker from the New York Republican Machine and had been instrumental in negotiating the unofficial agreements between the United States and Boulanger Regime. They would have preferred Platt, but saw many complications in getting him accepted by both the Congress and the public at large.

The second man was a curious choice because he was not a Republican and had been a long running thorn in the side of Root. Still, as Hay reasoned, the choice of the Governor of New York, Grover Cleveland, seemed logical and the benefits outweighed the liabilities. Cleveland had a reputation as a reformer and was mildly popular with the public. He was not exactly a supporter of the war, but at the same time, he was also not an outspoken critic. The votes and influence he could bring to Roots reelection bid could be what was required to finally put Debbs in his place. It would also go greatly towards silencing Hearst.

There were also other important factors besides appearing to form a coalition government. Both Root and Hay also wrote that they viewed Cleveland's chances of ever successfully running for the presidency as less than realistic. When you considered the additional benefit of removing Cleveland from his governorship and then putting him in a position where he could be controlled, it made the man the perfect choice to replace Knox. Unfortunately for Root, Congress disagreed and, to an extent, so did Cleveland who never truly accepted the offer to begin with.

On Capitol Hill, the cronies of William Jennings Bryan and his populists were not interested in replacing Knox with anyone. With Knox out of the way, the speaker of the house was next in line to become president. While no one even considered the possibility that Root would meet an untimely demise, just holding that particular key gave both the House of Representatives and the populists (aka former President Bryan) a very big negotiating chip that they could bring to the table when they needed it. As a result, the legislatures did everything they could to block the nomination of anyone to the

243

position, while appearing to only be interested in doing the very thing that they were trying to avoid.

This only served to make Root look indecisive and drove his campaign even further into the mud. It looked as if Debbs was going to win the election in November and move into the executive mansion in January of 1901. Then, just as it seemed that things could not get any worse, they did. The latest blow did not come from the political squabbling within the United States. It did not even come from North America. This came from Europe and suddenly grabbed the headlines so thoroughly that even the election took a back seat.

The Lance

It was only a little over a month after the LZ-4 had made her first combat patrol, over the city of Nancy, that an even larger force, with much larger Zeppelins, penetrated deep into France. It looked to many, the Kaiser included, that Von Zeppelin had pulled off a miracle.

The truth was that there was nothing magic about the sudden increase in the number of airships available to the German war machine. It had simply been foresight and careful planning. As the Germans had toyed with their prototypes, they were also setting up the machinery and organization along with gathering the raw materials to make many more. The only thing that held them back was a successful field test, and after LZ-4 they assumed that they had one.

LZ-4 would make three more combat missions before she was finally retired, scrapped, and her material reused to make other airships. While none of her missions resulted in anything that would alter the balance of the war, the Germans were gaining invaluable knowledge in powered flight and what to do with it. They were also taking every scrap of data of flight characteristics and putting it immediately to use. The engineers at their drawing boards, back in Bavaria, were quite often getting their data even before Schlieffen was getting his combat reports. Every new Zeppelin that the factories were turning out were much different and more advanced than the last one that made it out the hangar door.

It seemed rather odd, at least to the civilian populace of France, that the French military virtually ignored the German Zeppelins. Every Zeppelin attack made far more headlines than it did damage, so this is somewhat understandable. On the other side of that coin, and quite uncharacteristically, both Boulanger and his leading military commanders were in complete agreement on this matter. They considered the Zeppelins to be nothing more than a 'German toy' and their effects on the front as being militarily negligible. So far, as the facts seemed to indicate, they were correct in their assessment.

The fact that, quite often, one airship looked completely if not radically different from another one seemed to have left the French General Staff with the impression that they were all being handmade and had no real central coordination. The fact that the bombing capacity and range were proving to be extremely limited gave the impression of impotency. So, for Boulanger and his advisors, it appeared as if the Germans were wasting their time and resources and they were more than welcome to do so.

What they failed to see was that the Germans were testing their weapon to see what it was really capable of. The French failed to see that the rapidly increasing numbers proved that these weapons were not being haphazardly produced. The single biggest thing they failed to see was, the future, and the potential of airpower. This was all despite the fact that France was also working on its own military air project. It was something that, so far, Boulanger had paid as little attention to as he did the Zeppelins. The raid of May the 11th would change all of that for everyone. Its ramifications would be felt globally.

It is fair to say that the military significance of the air raid on Paris was much the same as the earlier raids at the front. There was very little in Paris that would hamper the war effort in general, and because of this many have labeled the attack as a terror raid. In some respects, this is true, but the Germans confined their attacks to militarily significant targets, most of which were various ministry buildings. They had yet to single out or attack any factories, because they did not believe that they could currently deliver enough damage to make it worth the effort.

Of course, two factors played into the reasoning behind the label of terror attack. The first was the simple fact that only one Zeppelin actually hit its target. The Germans had learned a great deal about making bombs in the intervening month and were now setting up factories to manufacture ordinance specifically for a later generation of airship. On May 11th, they were still using artillery shells, but had learned how to begin modifying them to make for better accuracy. They were also using larger shells, since even with the modifications, and the improved bomb sighting techniques, accuracy was still minimal at best.

The more serious improvement, and the one that gets the least attention, is the fact that the airships could even reach Paris in the first place. This was not only due to improved designs on fuel storage capacity and a general increase in engine performance, but German navigation skills over unfamiliar terrain were getting better as well. Still, they were not perfect, and this seems to have been the main reason for the target selection of both Paris and what to hit when they got there. The city was impossible to miss or mistake from the air. The targets selected were reasoned to be the most easily recognizable and biggest. Yet, despite this, almost all of the bombs missed their marks, and most of those landed on civilian homes and businesses.

One might think that this was the reason for the terror label, but in fact the newspapers outside of France almost entirely ignored the plight of the average Parisian. The terror label came from the one bomb that did hit and it likely found its mark simply because its target was impossible to miss. Most people were also completely unaware that the Eifel Tower was a legitimate military target even if it was far from an important one.

The tower was just over ten years old at this point and most had thought it would come down after the World's Fair that it was built for. It seems hard to believe today since the tower has become such an iconic landmark, but in the 1890's, it was at the center of a raging political firestorm. The simple fact was that a good number of Parisians considered it an eye sore and a few of those even went so far as to consider it an insulting monstrosity that was not only offensive to France, but even God. Strangely enough, the one group that harbored most of its detractors would be the one that saved it from the wrecking ball.

The French Army found a use for the tower. They had turned it into the single largest signal tower in the world. After the war broke out, huge semaphore flags were specifically manufactured for use on Eifel's grand vision of peace. They were constantly being hoisted and lowered at the top and with a good telescope they could almost be seen as far as the front lines. This was not exactly a military secret to anyone. It was just a dull little detail that the papers never picked up on, and as a result, almost no one outside of the French Army knew about it. Even pedestrians in Paris pretty much ignored the flags they saw flying from the tower. They certainly did not think about them when German bombs were falling on the city.

Fortunately for the tower, while it

might be an easy target to recognize, it was an extremely difficult target to hit. There were sixteen German Zeppelins that made the raid. Only thirteen actually reached Paris, and of those, three had been assigned to bomb the tower. One of those never even managed to get into a position of being able to release its payload. Winds and the other two Zeppelins kept getting in its way. They would eventually ditch their bomb on the way home.

The other two Zeppelins would unleash their full arsenal on the tower. They dropped over twenty high explosive shells that were converted munitions from a naval sixteen-inch gun. They left a good number of horrific looking craters around the tower that were highly photographed and widely distributed. It would be these craters that so horrified the civilian populations of the world. It was another great irony that the only bomb that actually hit the tower was virtually ignored because, like most of the ordinance, it failed to detonate.

Even if that bomb had gone off, it is very doubtful that it would have brought down the tower. It has even been speculated that the reason it buried itself in the ground beneath the base was because it hit some of the steel girders on the way down and that damaged the bombs ignition cap and spring. This will never be known for certain, but what we do know is that the tower itself was its best defense. The very nature of the tower makes it difficult to actually hit a critical load-bearing member, and the skeletal structure allows for the concussive force of the blast to bypass anything vital.

Of course, the Germans did not seem to care about this, or perhaps they were simply unaware. There could also be another reason and what happened after the bombing seems to suggest this. After LZ-19 expended her ordinance, the captain of the airship wanted one of the huge semaphore flags that was flying atop the tower as a war trophy. The flag itself seemed to give him the very data he needed (wind direction) in order to maneuver alongside. At worst, he figured he could get a piece of it, and if he was lucky then he could land some crewmen on the platform and steal the entire thing.

It did not quite go as planned. The French soldiers on the tower began shooting at LZ-19 as soon as it got within range, and this little bit of unnecessary bravado almost cost Germany one of her Zeppelins. Despite the failure of LZ-19, the little game of real life "capture the flag" indicates that the attack on the tower was more geared towards delivering a blow to the morale of the French populace than being a strike of military importance. If this is the case, then it failed. The city of Paris had never truly been a center of support for either Boulanger or what most Frenchman thought of as "Boulanger's war". Once they were attacked, personally, that began to rapidly change.

Another sudden realization struck the civilian populations of the world, and this was as true in Allied countries as it was in those of the Entente. Germany had invented a weapon that was a lance that could not only penetrate national defenses, but also ignore them altogether. This weapon could strike right at the heart of any country. How long would it be before every nation possessed this technology?

Even the French General staff could no longer ignore the Zeppelins.

More importantly was the fact that they no longer ignored their own project, the railroad engineer Chanute's attempt to build a heavier than air flying machine. It would seem that this aerial-plane, a name that most generals had a hard time understanding the origins of, was the logical defense against zeppelins. The real question that they were asking was, if the technology was even viable?

No one outside of the only three experimental airplane projects in the world knew the answer to that. In many ways, even those men did not. Chanute's attempts to achieve sustained flight in his base of operations, near Lyons, had failed to deliver anything close. His counterpart in the United States, Samuel Langley, had started out in Baltimore, but eventually relocated the American project to Wichita, Kansas. He seems to have been slightly ahead of Chanute in that his people had actually been able to get a prototype to stay in the air for all of twenty seconds under its own power. The problem was that they had not been able to reproduce their success and were not even sure how they did it in the first place.

The sudden panicked calls on both Chanute and Langley stressed the urgency of the new situation and one that neither man was able to do anything about. At least in the case of Langley, he did receive a substantial boost in actual support and funding. He was also promised anything and anyone he needed to get the job done. The reaction of the American government was not misplaced either. The fears that this technology would find its way across the Atlantic were not just unwarranted, they were a little too late.

Paniolo

The Germans had dutifully informed their allies of the Sky Train project from its inception. As we have already learned, the British had so thoroughly ignored it to the point that they might as well have never been informed in the first place. In defense of the British attitudes, at that time, even most Germans never believed it would work so, in some ways this is understandable. The British, like most modern militaries, actually had a balloon works at the time. It was dedicated to the manufacturing, testing, and deployment of small observation balloons that were organized in company sized units. After the Nancy raid by the LZ-4 its research and development section were expanded only slightly, but not given enough of a budget to accomplish very much. After Paris, the entire R&D was split off and relocated from Aldershot to the nearby city of Farnborough, where it was placed under the command of an up and coming army major by the name of Capper. The project would then, ultimately, be taken over by the Royal Navy and placed directly under the command of Admiral Fisher's office.

The British were only playing catch up. They had been caught as off guard as their enemies. The Confederates were an entirely different matter. Always with an eye towards anything that could offset the numerical advantage of their enemy, there were many at Mechanics Hall who saw potential in this new technology, even before it had ever been tried. The Confederacy also had their own ballooning facilities, which made them for both the Army and Navy, near

Williamsburg, Virginia. This new project, unlike that of the British, was never given to the ballooning Corps. The Confederate airship project started off as an entirely separate venture from the start.

The CSA also had its own heavier than air project. Much like those of their enemies, it had yet to produce any viable technology, but it already had an infrastructure. That project had ultimately been located in Florida, for three very sound reasons. The first was because most of central and south Florida was almost completely unpopulated. The second was because it was as far away from the United States as you could get in the CS. The last reason was the weather.

The leaders of the Confederate project needed a place with good headwinds in order to test their gliders. It was the same reason that Samuel Langley had wound up in Wichita and Chanute in Lyons. Langley was looking for the strong winds you encountered on the great plains, so he located near the largest Army depot in that region. Chanute was using the nearby cliffs and mountains of the Rhone River Valley. The Confederates preferred the beach and the warm gentle breezes coming off the Atlantic. They had initially tried to set up in a small town called Daytona, but eventually they moved to a nearby deserted cape that was called Cabo Canaveral.

The airship project was initially given to a young army Major by the name of Manget. Apparently, he was the third man to be offered the position and the first not to turn it down. Up until that point, Manget had spent the entire war working in the Confederate War Department at Mechanics Hall. His reason for taking the assignment was because he wanted to be anywhere but there. The reason for being offered the job was because he happened to be standing within sight of General Robert Lee Jr. when the first two men refused. Manget threw himself into the job with great enthusiasm, even after discovering that he would be reassigned to Florida. In the CSA, at that time, such a posting was akin to the Russians sending you to Alaska.

Manget lacked any serious qualifications for this job. He was a graduate of VMI, had a rudimentary understanding of engineering, and was in the military. That is as far as his qualifications went. He knew absolutely nothing of powered flight and was, apparently, unaware that anything was even remotely possible until the German raid on Nancy hit the newspapers. He had no idea that his own country was engaged in any kind of powered flight experiments until he got this job.

What Manget did prove to be was a more than competent administrator. He was also a quick study and had a near blank check in picking people to help him. His problem was very similar to that of the submarine project, only worse. There was no one in the CSA with any skills required to do this. Manget would have to start from scratch and find people with skills in doing other things that could be applied to an airship. Naturally, he thought he would find them at Canaveral, and he was sorely disappointed.

His first big shock was to discover that the person running the Confederate effort to build an airplane was not only a civilian, but a woman as well. She was a twenty-seven-year-old Texan by the name of Colleen "Kitty" Bean. After Manget met with her in Florida, he found that she was not only unimpressed with his project, but him as well. She also made no secret that she wanted him off her base. It was very clear that no help would be coming from this quarter, and Kitty's base, what little of it there was, seemed to be unsuitable to Manget's needs anyway.

Manget was soon to discover that he needed a location near a rail line and there were none that were running anywhere near Cabo Canaveral. That was the main reason he picked the city of Ocala as his main base. He settled in on some unused cattle pasture that was open, flat, and near the railroad. It also had the advantage of being free. The owner loaned the property to the Army in exchange for a tax break from the state. It would be the main reason that the airship crewmen, and eventually even their cargo, would eventually come to refer to themselves as the Sky Paniolo, or just Paniolo for short. That was a reference to the Floridian version of the Texas Cowboy. It also stood as a good cover name to confuse any enemy intelligence gathering.

The main reason that Manget

needed a rail line and would also give him a great jump on his goals was not logistical in nature. The Confederate State Department had managed to secure an actual Zeppelin from Germany. This was all done in the name of inter-allied cooperation; however, it must be noted that such goodwill between nation-states always comes with a price. In this particular case, it was a resource that the CSA had in abundance. Germany not only lacked this resource completely, but they now greatly coveted it.

The resource was a natural byproduct of oil drilling and for those in the oil business it was little more than a useless nuisance. For anyone wanting to fly an airship, it was the most important substance on Earth. This was the gas known as helium. The Germans had no sources of this, and as a result the Zeppelins were trapped into using the gas hydrogen to give them lift. The problem with hydrogen was that it was very flammable and highly combustible. It was the last thing you wanted to be near when bullets were flying.

As it turned out, hydrogen was not even safe under the most ideal conditions.

The Germans had already lost one airship
due to a static discharge which, as they
discovered to their horror, was the
natural byproduct of an airship with
constantly spinning propellers. It was
perfectly safe until you tried to land it, at
which point, you created man made
lightening. The Germans found a way
around this, and it was as simple as using
poles to ground the vehicle before
securing the mooring lines. This was very
dangerous work though and they were
desperate for a safer alternative. The
Confederates had the solution for this.

That was how LZ-7 found its way to
Florida, packed in sixteen freight cars. It
did not leave Manget with a sense of
optimism. Here was a vehicle that was
supposed to revolutionize transportation,
and it had been shipped across the
Atlantic on a British freighter and then
transported to its home base via a
railroad. It was a less than auspicious
start, and besides that the LZ-7 was a
design that the Germans had already
discarded. She had never even flown a
single combat mission and only had one
test flight under her belt before being
entirely scrapped.

The most important resource that came with the train was not actually the airship itself. Several German officers and engineers came along with it. Several British officers also arrived, one of them being the future head of their own project, John Capper. It was a lucky break for Manget, since none of his people spoke German and none of the Germans spoke English. It would be several of Capper's officers who had to do all the translating, and it was a position that Capper could live with. It made him privy to everything going on and put him in effective control of many things.

Of course, there would be a great deal of disagreement about how to proceed since Capper was exerting his advantage. Capper was also under orders to evaluate (meaning influence) the Confederate project and its value to assisting British interests in the western hemisphere (meaning the Royal Navy). Manget stuck to his guns, however. From the very inception of the project, sometime before the Nancy raid, the Confederates had some radically different ideas about what to do with any potential airship. The attack by LZ-4 only encouraged Manget, because, despite the headlines, it was clear that the damage done by bombing was minimal. The Confederacy could never hope to build as many airships as Germany, so they had to get the biggest bang for their buck.

Manget's persistence paid off. It took a good number of calls to his superiors and much haggling with his allies, but by the time of the Paris raid, his project had already bore fruit. The LZ-7 was no longer the LZ-7 and that was more than just in name. Manget cannibalized the German airship and along with new parts that he acquired from a number of sources, had built the CSS Thunder.

Unlike most of the German fleet, the Thunder was a rigid framed design. It was also longer than the original LZ-7, had two enclosed gondolas, and even had the look of what modern airships would become. More importantly, it used helium for its lift capacity, and it was equipped with some of Astin Green's newer, lighter, and more powerful truck engines. This gave the Thunder a better range and more maneuverability than any airship at that time.

That is not to say that the Thunder lacked problems. Because of the specialized nature of its payload, which was the reason for its larger size, Thunder was more at the mercy of the elements. The principals of aerodynamics were only now just being discovered, and the learning curve was usually measured in lives. The Thunder had a less than optimal shape for flying and her surface produced considerable drag. While underway this could be dealt with, but it made landing her particularly dangerous and that was even in the best of conditions. This was of great importance to the fledgling Confederate airship fleet. Landings in less than optimal conditions was a high priority, and in fact the difficulty involved in this maneuver almost put an end to the entire project.

The salvation of the Confederate effort would come from what might seem a logical source, but at the time it was the most unforeseen of places. The CSA, and specifically the state of Virginia, had an obsession about the territories that it considered occupied by the United States. The most prominent of these was what the US now called the state of West Virginia. The area has extremely mountainous terrain, and as the reasoning went at Mechanics Hall, in order to fight on mountains, you need mountain troops.

The result of this thinking were two mountain warfare schools, one in North Georgia near the town of Toccoa and the other in Gatlinburg, Tennessee. By the time of the war they had managed to produce a viable battalion of specialized soldiers who allegedly had the skills to operate in the kind of terrain that was most common in West Virginia. By 1900, this battalion had done very little. They were too small to operate on their own and, so far, had seen only limited combat. Even when they did, they were used primarily as support troops in the capacity of combat engineers.

After Manget and his staff had done some research, it became quickly obvious that this mountain unit had the set of skills required to solve most of their problems. Each man had at least a minimum of demolition training, but that was not even the main concern. What was important was that each man was an expert at getting up and down a rope. This seemed to offer a solution to the problem of landing in a location that was not prepared for an airship. This was important because these soldiers were to be the ship's primary weapon, and in order for them to be effective, they had to be able to get to the ground and then be recovered. Manget was surprised to find that the mountain soldiers were not only receptive, but eager to try out his plan.

Thunder Over Cincinnati

By the time that the news of the Paris raid had reached Richmond, Manget had already been agitating the War Office to try out his operation. Exactly why Mechanics Hall was hesitant is really unclear, but it seems likely that the primary reason was because very few people in the war office even knew that the CSS Thunder existed. Even President Wheeler was in the dark and quite miffed that his Generals had never bothered to mention this before now. The Paris raid ended any debate and shined a spotlight on the entire project. Manget was given the green light he had been waiting on, and he wasted no time setting the wheels in motion. His airship and his troops were leaving their base and moving north no sooner than he got his telegram to go.

Their primary target was sitting right on the Ohio river between the cities of Cincinnati, Ohio, and Covington, Kentucky. Until the opening of the Brooklyn Bridge, the J. Roebling Bridge had been the largest suspension bridge in the world. It was one of several primary arteries across the river and of strategic importance in supplying the front lines in Kentucky and Tennessee. The Confederate plan was simple. They were going to drop it in the river and not only cut off the north/south traffic but also block the river traffic with its wreckage.

The plan sounded simple enough, but to the chagrin of the Confederate strike team, it was far more complicated than it looked. The first problem they encountered was the weather. They found themselves stuck for three extra days at their staging area near Lafayette, Tennessee. The lack of weather information combined with the normal torrential storms of the late spring almost put an end to the operation before it even began.

The weather was a problem that was overcome by simply waiting for a stretch of clear skies. No one could actually know about the weather over the target, so no one worried about it. The real problems were yet to come and then only after the operation was underway. While many of these snags might seem to be a lack of planning, the truth of the matter was that no one had ever attempted such an operation before. As simple as it looked on the surface, it was anything but that in actual execution.

So much effort had gone into getting the assault team to its target that almost no thought had been given to what they should do once they were there. That is not to say that the Confederates had completely ignored the tactical concerns. They had just oversimplified the requirements. They never considered exactly how hard it is to destroy a bridge of that size. Modern calculations have revealed that they did not bring enough explosives with them, and as a result no matter what happened on the ground Roebling was going to stay up.

The first part of the Confederate plan went well enough. The Thunder dropped its troops in the dark and well short of the bridge. It was a spectacular success, because up until that point, every single attempt to repel from the rear gondola had resulted in someone getting injured and even one death. The forty-seven man strike team landed with all of its gear and proceeded towards the bridge. That was the first and last thing that would go according to plan.

Despite the fact that the Roebling was a major artery, no one in the planning of the operation ever seemed to consider that the bridge would be in use. It was not only in use but choked with traffic. Perhaps they thought the darkness would mean a lack of traffic, but they were very wrong. The Confederates did luck out in one aspect. No infantry or other types of combat troops were moving across the bridge when they finally managed to begin the assault. There were guards of the Ohio Territorial Militia, but at least the Confederates were expecting them and had a plan.

Unfortunately, the diversion did not go as expected. The CSS Thunder was the diversion, and as per the plan she crossed over the river and even managed to loiter around just north of the bridge. Given the recent events in Paris, there was no one who was just gazing at the airship. Not only were the bridge guards shooting at the Thunder, but it seemed as if nearly everyone in Cincinnati was running to their roof and joining them. The heavy volume of unexpected fire forced the Confederate airship to back off and gain some altitude so it would be out of range of the small arms.

The other problem was that it only distracted the guards on the north side of the bridge. The troops on the south side were now alerted, and that was where the Confederate ground team began their assault. Some unknown US officer also called in for the reaction team, and by the time the Confederates got there, the US position had been reinforced. This led to a shoot out on the Kentucky side that involved a very high volume of bullets in a congested area. Civilians who just happened to be crossing the bridge were not playing victim either. Many of them joined in the fight.

With this in mind, it is rather

surprising that the Confederates managed to do as well as they did. They actually overran the perimeter defenses and seized a small portion of the south span before being stopped by the Ohio militia. They even managed to detonate some of their charges, but the damage to the bridge was minimal. After almost an hour of fighting, the Confederates were running low on ammunition, and the US troops were getting a constant stream of reinforcements on both sides of the bridge. The Confederate mountain troops were forced to withdraw. The most surprising aspect of this was that the only ones who pursued them were civilians that they easily kept at bay. The surviving members of the assault team were eventually and successfully winched back on the Thunder, and the Confederate airship did make it back to friendly lines with no further incidents.

The attack was instant worldwide news and something of a shock to the people of the United States. Eugene Debbs wasted no time lambasting President Root for being monumentally incompetent for allowing such a thing to happen. At this point it seemed as if Root's reelection bid was doomed and, with it, the cause of the

Triple Entente.

On the other side of the front lines, despite the tactical failure, the citizens of the Confederacy were drunk with the elation of success. They now seemed to have a grand new weapon that no one else did, and despite its shortcomings people were mostly of the opinion that next time they would do better. While the civilians might have felt this way, the Confederate military was a bit more subdued in their reaction. They had very mixed feelings about the Cincinnati Raid and with good reason. They were not, however, so pessimistic as to shut the program down or keep Manget from taking another go at it.

Unfortunately, the reaction in the US was enough to prevent another raid on any bridge over the Ohio river. The guards at each crossing were tripled and this easily put them beyond the abilities of the Confederates to attack with a vertical assault. The Confederate airship program would also be dealt a serious blow when in late summer, while moored at her hangar in Ocala, a hurricane destroyed both the Thunder and its shelter. The home of the CSS air fleet would relocate to Northern Alabama after that. It would delay the CSA program for months.

The most lasting effects of the raid were completely unseen in its immediate aftermath. They were the kinds of things that cannot be planned for or even expected. The first of these was the presence of a particular individual on that morning. He was a member of the Ohio Territorial Guard. Born in Michigan of immigrant parents, his name was Frank Zholhus. Frank was in his late twenties and had long since served his time in the regular army. He was somewhat angered when after the war broke out, he found himself being drafted back into the military, specifically the Ohio militia system as a part time reservist. He was required to give three months a year to military missions inside the state. In May of 1900, his job was guarding the Roebling Bridge.

The other effect was the presence of yet another individual. His name was Paul Laurence Dunbar, who was a relatively successful poet and writer with publications in such periodicals, as Harpers Weekly. Dunbar was a native of Kentucky, and more importantly he was also the son of former slaves. To put it simply, Dunbar was a black man. On that morning, he was driving his buggy and fighting traffic on the Roebling bridge. He had just returned from visiting friends in Dayton. Due to Dunbar's ill health (he was suffering from the first stages of tuberculosis), one of those friends chose to accompany him on the journey home. This man was the owner of a moderately successful bicycle shop, and his name was Wilbur Wright.

The two men were caught in the fire of the initial Confederate assault and forced to flee northwards on foot. The exact details of what happened after that are unclear. What we do know is that Dunbar took a bullet wound in the chest and it punctured his left lung. He died in the arms of Wilbur, as they both sheltered from the hail of fire under a wagon. Wilbur would survive the battle and eventually make it back home. He also returned with an attitude that both surprised and shocked his siblings. This change of heart was completely unknown at the time, or at least it was outside of the Wright family. However, before this chain of events would reach its inevitable conclusion, the entire world would know.

Illusions

What the raid on the Roebling Bridge had done, in a very dramatic way was to bring the war home to the civilian population of the United States. Not since Washington had the population of a major American city been subjected to the horrors of war. By the summer of 1900, Washington had been largely forgotten, and the Confederates had given up shelling it in favor of tactical targets closer to the front lines. It is also noteworthy that, despite its importance as a capital, Washington was at that time a medium sized city at best and of little economic value to the US. The fact was simply that most of the American population did not live there, and it seemed as far off a place as Fashoda when they read about it in the newspapers.

Suddenly, if the enemy wanted to kill you, they could just drop right out of the sky and do it. They no longer had to get by your army, and this was a frightening prospect to most people who knew little of military matters. The truth was far less dramatic, and in fact, it was in many ways the exact opposite of what it appeared to be. In the summer of 1900, the Allies were winning one headline after another. The problem with this is that winning battles is far more important, and here, the Entente had a clear advantage.

Their armies were not exactly winning, but they were making far better progress than the allies. The wonder weapons that grabbed entire pages in the newspapers had not really managed to even make a dent in changing the actual situation. That was why military planners were far less optimistic and far more cautious about their uses. The fact was that up until now no strategists were even sure if these new weapons would be of any value at all. Sure, their future potential was realized, but in order for that to happen you first had to have a future. By mid-1900, there were some who suspected that their nations might not. Some even craved that possibility.

The word civilization was invented by the Romans. Its meaning, more or less, was a human society that was based on people living in cities. At the time, when Rome first began to be a prominent player in the politics of their region, the differences between city dwellers and those who chose the rural life were vast. The newfound power of the cities and the revolutionary capabilities that these organizations enabled, were responsible for creating many new ideas. This created new problems and the chosen Roman solution was to "civilize' the rural folks. The events of the 19th century bare some resemblance to the mechanisms that were turning in the time that Rome transitioned from republic to empire.

While the emergence of the Roman Empire was the ultimate result of city life coming to dominate other forms of human lifestyles, it took several millennia before an equally powerful invention came along and caused yet another substantial shift that, yet again, favored the city rat over the country mouse. This invention did not begin in the 19th century, but it was most certainly at the very heart of this war. It was the Industrial Revolution, something that had its groundwork laid in the middle ages and began sprouting by the 17th century. At the dawn of the 20th, it had become unstoppable and its ceiling was yet to be seen. It also caused massive social disruptions that most people of the Victorian World never truly understood and, indeed, few people even do today.

The Industrial Revolution caused a fundamental demographic shift. People were leaving their farms and rural lives in record numbers and migrating to the big cities which promised better jobs, pay, and lifestyles that looked far more interesting. The result of all this was a change in the basic needs, for a lot of people, and very quickly. It appeared to many that the old rules were no longer working and they had no idea why. In many ways, this perception seems to have had merit and in others it did not. What is undisputable was that in this time of social chaos, soap box, street corner pundits were offering a wide variety of solutions and most of them for the right price.

Over time, these new ideas began to coalesce into a few distinct camps where they began to organize and grow. Some of the terminology of this era such as left- and right-wing political leanings are still with us today. Some of the very movements are still with us as well, even if the conditions that spawned them are long since gone. There were really only two things that all of these new philosophies seemed to agree on. The first was that there needed to be a new way of doing things. The second was that the guys who did it the old way needed to be gone. It was the answers to the questions of what and how that divided these schools of thought.

On the other side of the equation, the people who represented the old ways were not about to go willingly. It is human nature to root for the underdog, and due to this factor it makes them, the Emperors and Kings, the Presidents and Industrialists, look like bad guys. The only problem with this view is that just because someone is on top, does not automatically make them evil and/or stupid. The Victorian age was a very autocratic one, and for the world at large it was one that actually worked. One might despise dictators and absolute power, but the monarchs, along with the systems that maintained their power had actually managed to keep the peace for nearly a century. That was an accomplishment that is quite rare in human history. The majority of their subjects also prospered in this same time period.

This might prompt the question of exactly why was there so much unrest? The answer seems to go right back to the age old rural versus city conflict that has been waged since humans first started settling down in permanent homes. Most of the monarchs of the time, no matter where you looked, were evolutions of governments formed to run rural agrarian societies. This was most certainly true of European, Chinese, and Japanese cultures. Ironically, the two that were not were African and Indian. In the 19th century, neither of these civilizations ruled themselves, so they played little part in the global power struggles of the time. The most dominant was, of course, European, and most of their troubles can be traced right back to one thing. Nations that embraced industrial ideas and technologies, and worked at incorporating them into their infrastructure, fared much better than those that did not.

The wild card in all of this was the very same thing that Wolseley reported to the Salisbury cabinet in his statistical analysis regarding the causes of the war. This was the United States. The Americans were Europeans in all but name, yet their geographical circumstances had allowed them to accomplish something that was impossible in Europe. They had largely discarded the political system that was based on heretical castes and reinvented the older system that was once favored by European city states, the Republic. The original revolutionaries of the 18th century had actually thought that their revolution would spread beyond the confines of North America and liberate the world (or at least Europe which was all they cared about).

While it is a little-known fact today, this almost happened. The French Revolution was a direct consequence of the American. At the same time, in the power vacuum that was 18th century Germany, many new republics sprang into existence. They were all emulating the Americans. They also destroyed themselves. The ironic twist is that France did not produce a republic, but a dictator. This man was Napoleon, and some of his first actions were to stomp the new

German republics flat. It was quite disheartening to many of the American revolutionaries like for example Thomas Jefferson who was an avid supporter of both France and Napoleon. Then came 1861.

The birth of the Confederate States seemed as if the experiment in republicanism had completely failed. The argument that was being made by many autocrats was that a mass of people could not effectively govern themselves and the American 61 seemed to prove this. It was not something that they knew, it was more of a feeling. It was very obvious because by the time of the war it was undisputable that America was no longer playing its democracy card. The name of the game was now to beat everyone else at their own game. To put it in a word, the United States had become motivated by revenge.

This was not something that was ever lost on the Confederate States even if it took some time for her allies to notice. It was only one of many things that was quite ironic about the CSA. For one thing, her people arguably maintained the attitude that the USA no longer did. Her people felt as if they were the rightful inheritors of the republican traditions despite the fact that they were inarguably the largest slave holding state left in the modern world. Of course, to classical eyes that is not as much a contradiction as it is to modern ones. Both Athens and Rome, the inspiration for the current democracy, had the institution of slavery at their peak. Unfortunately for the CSA, they were not living in the classical world.

Despite the fact that it was quite obvious that slavery was in its death throes at the dawn of the twentieth century, it seemed to matter very little. Even if slavery had become quite rare, just the fact that it legally existed was enough to complicate nearly every aspect of life in the Confederacy and that included her military and foreign affairs. Again, the only reason for this seems to have been nothing more than an overwhelming sense of pride. In this much, from rich to poor, the white citizens of the Confederacy seemed to be in complete agreement. They simply did not wish to admit that they had been wrong. This was at a time when even the staunchest Home Party stalwart had to recognize that slavery was no longer economically viable, and even a case could be made that it never had been.

The most ironic thing about the situation was that slavery had simply been a byproduct of the most overwhelming factor that had driven everything in that region since the Europeans first arrived. It was not economy, since the resources of the land were minimal at best. It was not the social factors even if they were what immediately drew in the eye. One word could describe almost all human activities in the region for several centuries and that was, security. It was the single most important factor that started with the British Empire, then transferred to the United States, and then eventually to the people who actually lived there in the form of the Confederate States.

The original large-scale use of slaves was by the British. This was directly due to their absolute critical need of pine tar that was mostly found in South Carolina. Their primary source, Finland, had been compromised by a war between Russia and Sweden. Without this tar microbes that thrived in tropical waters where their ships now routinely traveled would eat the ships hulls and destroy the British fleet. It was a serious concern along with one other. The region was also required as a buffer zone to protect the more prosperous colonies to the north.

This was the situation inherited by the United States, only they lacked the power of the British Empire. What had been a buffer for Britain was, to the young American nation, an open invitation to invasion by larger predatory countries that had already proven that this was exactly what they intended. The only way the Americans could fortify their nearly nonexistent southern border was to thoroughly populate the region, but once again it was resource poor. It made attracting colonists difficult in the best of times.

That was how the plantation system grew up. It was the only way to make the region economically viable, but still the area suffered from what it always had since the British first discovered their need for pine tar. It was the lack of a manual labor force, and both pine harvesting and the plantation economies required exactly that. This made slave labor critical and placed a demand on the trade which effected regions way beyond North America. A little understood situation, even today, was that Africa was recovering from the collapse of a major empire (much like Europe had after the fall of Rome), and the sudden demand for slaves only retarded their recovery, as it drove hostile factions in the sub-Saharan region into outright war in order for some groups to cash in on the new gold mine.

What it also did was put the Confederacy in an awkward situation from the very first day of its existence. Its strategic situation was unalterable since this was largely geographic. Its economy was all but impossible without a labor force that its allies and enemies, alike, found repugnant. At the same time, this economic reality made its social system highly chaotic and that required an autocratic authority to keep it in line while, at the same time, it maintained its democratic government. It was a giant balancing act on a high wire that was essential, because all of it was required to maintain the economy, which, going right back to the start, was directly tied to its security.

This was not just a problem for the

CSA. Its very existence made the USA vulnerable to not only an ideological debate, but more importantly to its physical security as well. Events seemed to have proven that. When viewed in these terms, it is quite understandable why the USA chose the path that it did, one that unquestionably led to the outbreak of the war. It also had far more subtle implications for the rest of the world that in the end were far more powerful. We're only now just coming to terms with this.

As long as the United States seemed successful, it represented a certain measure of hope to people all over the world. This might seem an overstatement, but you have to remember that this was a world where the majority of humanity could not even hope to have a say in the course of larger events that shaped their lives, not to mention their very survival. Even if it were not entirely true, the idea that you could go to this place called America and possibly have some kind of say was a powerful one for many. It had to be lingering in the back of people's minds as they formed little groups to agitate for change. Now, this seemed to be not entirely dead, but somehow different.

At the same time, the Confederacy was a boon to the autocrats of the world where they saw a system that was similar to their own, and prospering, despite its physical handicaps and chaotic domestic life. In fact, it could be easily argued that the problems faced by the CSA were all too similar to states like Austria Hungary and Imperial Mexico. You could even make a case that it was very similar to China and even in many ways to Czarist Russia. While it would go too far to say that the Confederacy was some kind of role model, it most definitely was a case that someone like Franz Joseph or Nicholas Romanov would point to and say, "See, see what happened to the Americans."

Toasters, Bulbs, And Bullets

The social and political ramifications of the war were only just starting to take shape as the second anniversary drew near. They were obvious, but as of yet, no one had dreamed they would directly impact the ongoing military operations. That is not to imply that this was a new development in the annals of military history. Those factors had always been there, but were rarely noticed by military men who were very technical professionals and quite often oblivious to anything that was not an immediate concern on the battlefield. What had changed was not just the industrialization of war, but in the course of the 19th century the art of mass killing had been turned into a science that wielded statistics as a weapon as often as it did a rifle. The men who crunched numbers were starting to see a few things that had been overlooked in the centuries past.

The factor that caught the attention of the military mathematicians first, and indeed greatly impacted the social climate, were the economic issues that were a direct result of the conflict. In this case, it was not because anyone had ignored or overlooked it. Every government had some kind of plan that dealt with the issues of protecting their economy while attacking that of the enemy. What no one had managed to do was to understand the scale and shape that this silent war would take. I choose the word silent, because this aspect of the war was not being waged in the newspapers, and this also included the presses of the nations that were free to print what they chose.

That would also impact the social, and it was a great irony of the war in that the only ones printing anything about it were social agitators and small political extremists groups who devoted much ink to hand bills that with hindsight seemed to be uncharacteristically accurate given the source. It was once noted, by former Confederate President James Longstreet, that the easiest day for a propagandist is, "The day he only has to print the truth". With this in mind, it must be noted that the political and social agitators were having a very easy time with the war. It was also the reason no one listened to them. The best way to lose an argument is to overstate your case, and that is exactly what these small groups had been doing for years. People no longer believed anything they had to say, and this included things that were obviously true.

Yet with even more irony, the one group that knew these handbills were not only accurate, but barely scratched the surface of the growing problem were the people that the authors of the bills wanted to replace. By the summer of 1900, the national leaders of every nation on Earth had already seen the facts and they did not wish to advertise any of it. This was as true for the remaining neutrals as it was for the belligerents. The fact was that severe shortages were on the way, and there was nothing anyone could do about it.

The problem was not one of production, and this allowed the major powers to keep a lid on the information for some time. Despite many claims after the war, the increase in the military over civilian consumption had little to do with the shortages and rationing. The reason for this seems to be the pressure the war was putting on the industrialized infrastructure. Demand on manufacturers were increasing, and the materials they had to work with were rapidly going in the opposite direction.

In a normal supply and demand market, this would usually just result in extremely high prices, but this is not what happened or at least not on the military side. Governments held their industrialists to fixed prices and only increased them when it became clear that this situation would cause a business to collapse. In effect, even in nations that had a free market their entire industrial infrastructure had become practically nationalized for the duration of the war. This gave some short-term advantages to the belligerent powers, but these measures would result in long term social and economic turmoil that would echo for decades to come.

Needless to say, the situation forced the manufacturing sectors to imply new methods, try new ideas, and streamline their efforts in order to survive this new situation. If they did not, then they were liable to become casualties of the war despite the fact that not a single explosive or attack had yet to strike a heavily industrialized region. That is how the industrialists became the first ones, beyond the governments, to really notice what the true problem was. The world transportation net was slowly breaking down.

While governments had expected such problems, they had failed to grasp both the nature and scope. They understood that they would lose resources from regions that were now hostile. They understood that transportation would become more expensive as both raw materials and finished products would have to be rerouted. They knew they would lose considerably more transported materials than was common in peace time. What they did not count on was the naval quagmire.

After the battle of the Yellow Sea, no major power was willing to risk their primary battle fleets. Indeed, as we shall see, the only major naval actions after that point were forced on the belligerents out of desperation as opposed to a carefully planned strike. To have a fleet crippled or destroyed could easily cost either side the war, and it was a fact that everyone was all too aware of. This left the sea in a near state of anarchy. It also left both sides nipping at each other's heels as they attempted to disrupt enemy merchant shipping while protecting their own.

As the major powers discovered, neither side in the war had a clear-cut advantage as the strengths and weaknesses were canceling each other out. It became a field day for commerce raiding, as fast attack cruisers could wreak havoc on the unarmed merchant ships that were too numerous and widespread to be completely protected by anyone. In the first year of the war nearly every unguarded sea lane, of which there were many, had come to a standstill.

This also included those of many neutral nations (and was most definitely a factor in Italy's entrance into the war), who would lose far fewer ships than those of the belligerents, but it mattered little in the grand scheme of things. In most cases, their losses were not enough to warrant joining the conflict, but more than enough for them to have to stop their shipping. Most of these small nations also lacked the ability to form protective convoys which was the only real counter to the threat of privateers. As a result, a great deal of hauling tonnage would sit out the war in various neutral ports around the world.

The nations that did have the ability to offer protection to their shipping fleets faired only slightly better. There were never enough warships to adequately guard them all. Convoys almost always produced stray ships that could either not keep up or got lost for various reasons. Many enemy cruisers would follow the convoys and stay well within visual range, but just outside the range of the guns that protected it. These raiders would then quickly pounce on any vessel that got out of formation.

It proved to be impossible to hide the convoy schedules, and worst of all they were terribly slow. The swift warships that protected the cargo haulers found themselves at the mercy of the slowest buckets in their small groups. Most of these civilian ships were built for cost, and as a result they were not terribly fast or adequately protected from even the most mundane conditions that were standard in combat operations. The speed of their engines was also only one factor in their general mobility. Convoys had to be assembled and doing this in the best of conditions is not so simple. When you're dealing with many ships that all have their own time schedules and concerns, there is no rushing it.

The ultimate result of this was that even when losses to the enemy did not slow down the transfer of goods, the simple rate of transfer was drastically reduced. Naturally, due to this situation the governments took control of the cargo manifests and prioritized them according to their needs with militarily significant goods getting priority over everything else. This would begin to exacerbate many of the problems on land, as the war planners had yet to factor in the social disruptions, many of which were unforeseeable.

One fact that definitely escaped all of the collective information of the statisticians was the fact that most of the industrialized economies had grown into consumer markets that relied greatly on any number of highly specialized goods. There is no better product to illustrate this than something as simple and taken for granted as the light bulb. The market for electrical products, and its two competing forms, alternating and direct currents, was rapidly expanding and seemed limitless. Many an industrialist knew that this market was the key to untold wealth and were eager to get in on the ground floor. The light bulb was quite literally lighting the path to the future. The war was dimming its prospects.

Most major cities in the industrialized nations had active power plants by 1900. These were used to power any number of devices, but the most common was artificial lighting and that required the bulbs. The light bulb had become so common that its availability had already become taken for granted in cities. Even in modern times, light bulbs have a reputation for quickly burning out and uneven quality. This was definitely the case at the turn of the 20th century. Without a constant supply of the bulbs the wires hanging from most kitchen and common room ceilings were effectively useless to the average family.

The first shortages of the bulbs show up on the historical record in several ads that appeared in the New York Times in the spring of 1899. There was another feature that was becoming common to the consumer market at the time, and this was the department store. Several of these including one of the most successful of the lot, Tiffany's, placed competing advertisements announcing that they had a sale on light bulbs. This would not be so unusual except that none of these stores ever sold such items before now. Most people had become accustomed to buying this product at either hardware, general, or dry good stores along with the occasional specialty shop. Now it seemed the department stores had managed to grab a significant portion of the supply because, as they reasoned, that supply was dwindling and high profits were to be made.

There was also another and somewhat darker reason that the big stores got into the electricity business, and it was perhaps due to a little known casualty of the war. Macy's had been the store that started the light bulb wars in New York City, and their reason for doing so had nothing to do with selling the actual bulbs. Macy's had found a niche that boosted its sales at the end of every year. It was promoting a holiday that had been growing in popularity since the mid-19th century. It was an old holiday called Christmas and one that had been largely ignored in the English-speaking world for centuries.

A German Prince, who happened to be married to Queen Victoria, was the person who made the holiday gain notoriety when he brought his boyhood traditions to Buckingham palace and put up a Christmas Tree that captivated the imagination of the public. Department stores on both sides of the Atlantic were quick to realize the implications of the gift giving aspect of the tradition, and they would begin to heavily promote it. Within twenty years Christmas was paired with new technologies, mainly electricity and the light bulb, which made it safe and affordable for everyone to light up a Christmas tree along with their homes and businesses. By the time of the war the fad was growing, and the holiday was as popular as ever. It was not entirely standard in everyone's mindset, however.

Macy's department store realized the implications of not having the ability to light up a Christmas tree which would dissuade many from celebrating the holiday. Indeed, the war had already taken its toll just from the simple fact that people were now far more concerned with day to day issues. They could also ill afford the brand-new consumer products that were becoming ever more common before the war. Macy's sales were taking a nosedive. Christmas was important to them because their name had become almost synonymous with the holiday.

Their plans to horde the bulbs did not work out either. Not only did the sudden influx of sales from the competitors force them to begin selling the supplies that they were stockpiling for December, but the US Government became involved. Eventually Macy's had no choice but to sell off their supplies, and as a result people were no longer decorating for the holiday. Christmas would eventually fizzle out like a bad bulb and Macy's right along with it. The department store would go out of business in less than ten years. Their plans for a parade, their annual pageantry, and their huge productions would all vanish into the annals of history and be forgotten. Christmas would go back to being a holiday of drunks and loafers as it had been a century before.

It was not just the fact that the bulb was an essential element to modern life (and war production). It was not that the bulb required a complex process to manufacture. The single biggest problem that created the shortages was the fact that many of the needed materials to create them, particularly in the filament coils, had other more critical uses in the manufacture of war materials. While a good deal of the material was common in many nations, it only took the lack of one substance to make the product either cost more or impossible to manufacture at all.

At least the light bulb survived. Its utility was simply too valuable to everyone. Other products were not so lucky. The electric toaster was such a product. It was the result of much effort by those who were looking for ways to exploit the new technology for commercial purposes. It was very new just before the war and had become something of a fad. The idea of deliberately burning one's bread had caught on. It had been done before the toaster, but was labor intense and took someone that knew what they were doing. As a result, toast was largely on the menus of the wealthy and by and large a luxury item. The electric toaster, like the bulb to Christmas trees, had changed all of that, or at least until you could no longer find them for purchase.

The heating elements, the coils, and even the cases were all made of materials that were, for the time, very high tech. That was not even factoring in the insulation for the electric plugs which were made of rubber. The shortages of that particular substance, most of which came from neutral Holland's colony in the south Pacific, was almost universal in the industrialized nations. It also had multiple and critical military applications that would only grow as the war went on. This factor would doom any number of consumer products. As a result, the toaster, and the fad that it created would quickly vanish, never to return.

Such casualties of war seem like very small things. In fact, most of them were. The problem was that while each change was small, their collective weight was enormous. They were impacting attitudes and perceptions. People were slowly realizing that the old days were gone, and that the new century was going to be very different from the one they were leaving behind. This changed their behaviors which also included their spending habits. Just like with Macy's, many businesses began to notice this only to discover one horrifying fact. They could not change to meet their customers new habits. The war simply would not allow it.

It was a disaster waiting to happen and the only thing holding it back were the war policies of the various world governments. It meant that even after hostilities were concluded, like the child with his finger plugging the leak of a dam, they could not release the control of their infrastructure without it collapsing all around them. Above all else, this would set the tone for the next century, and it became the most lasting and least known consequence of the world war.

Waves Over Waves

It is yet another great irony that what gave the allies one of its greatest weapons was a man who was a citizen of a nation that they found themselves at war with. It was quite fortunate for them that a twenty-one-year-old electrical engineer from Italy, by the name of Guglielmo Marconi, had chosen to visit Great Britain less than two years before hostilities broke out. It was a further irony that this trip was both suggested and facilitated by another man who was not only a citizen of an enemy of Great Britain, but even an honorary official of the United States Government. While being ironic, it is however, not surprising that a young Marconi and his mother would make the trip. Even Marconi's own government had turned a blind eye to his break through and the only official in Rome that even knew about it had labeled the report as, "for the loony bin," and not given it another second's thought.

Marconi had traveled to Great Britain for one reason only. He was looking for money. None was forth coming in Italy, and Marconi had managed to do something amazing for the time, and unbelievable to anyone outside of the academic pursuits of physics. His trip would be successful in that he found his patron before he had even cleared customs in Dover. Marconi had brought his equipment with him, and upon inspection of their cases the customs officials immediately recognized that this might be something important. They had long since been alerted to look for any new technology that was entering Britain. It was quite a tall order considering that Marconi was not exactly unique in his quest for funds. The difference was, unlike Marconi's equipment, most of the other potentials would never amount to anything.

The Royal Navy was very quick to oblige Marconi an audience. Once again, Marconi proved to be lucky since in 1896 the admiralty was a little less than progressive. He was fortunate that one of his many demonstrations was to the royal post office and its chief engineer, a Welshman by the name of William Preece. He was a man that was familiar with the theories behind the contraption that Marconi had brought with him. He was also very impressed because it seemed that this contraption proved many theories that Preece had developed while working on standard telegraphs and under water cables that now linked the continents. This would be ironic in that these theories, which were much supported by Preece, would not only be wrong, but sound much like the magical musings of Merlin rather than science, or at least they would to a modern ear.

Marconi's work would rapidly progress as he would eventually receive funding, resources, and support from not only the Royal Navy but several civilian agencies as well. Despite this, the Navy was unwilling to use any of it until a certain Admiral, Jackie Fisher, was reassigned from the Caribbean to the

Ordinance Bureau and first heard of this marvelous new "toy". It was something of a miracle that Fisher became aware of the project since very few that were outside of Marconi's lab even knew it existed.

This fact seems to suggest that the older Admirals took this invention seriously enough and actually believed that, one day, it might actually work. How could they not? They received regular updates on Marconi's progress. They kept very tight security around the project, and this was aided by the fact that it seemed ridiculously fantastical to begin with. Anyone outside the project, who did hear about it, simply scoffed like those back in Italy.

Fisher, whose career began in a navy that had nothing but wooden warships and muzzle loading cannon had seen enough change to form the belief that just about anything was possible. As soon as he was promoted to Second Admiral, in the wake of the disaster at Yellow Sea, he was following Marconi's work daily and now he had the authority to employ this power. This would not be long before he discovered the existence of the German flying trains.

If Tirpitz had an almost insurmountable problem of explaining to Fisher the idea of a steel locomotive with wings, then Fisher's task was near impossible in trying to get across the idea of what the British had labeled the, "lightening detector". The name hailed from Marconi himself and it had been the original idea and success behind his work. The British kept the name for security reasons and used it to casually refer to the project. Why anyone would even want to detect lightening was, initially at least, beyond the Germans. Apparently, this was the case for everyone else because the security on the project was never breeched. While this new technology really did do as the name suggested, its potential was far greater. Today we call this technology, the radio.

Despite what is commonly accepted, in 1900 the radio was not a new idea. Work had been going on to make a successful 'wireless telegraph' for almost five decades at this point. This work was going on in virtually every nation on the planet and had started no sooner than some physicists realized you could build a device that detected magnetic radiation.

Today, we simply call that static and find it annoying. In 1854, when it was first discovered, people stood in lines to listen to it for as long as they could. It was simply a curiosity though. The real trick would be to manipulate those waves into something useful. Magnetic waves could be generated so many scientists realized this was not an impossible dream. Unfortunately for people like Marconi, who understood this, very few people outside of academia did.

The real problem, almost from the start, was not in the generation or reception of the radiation. The real problem was one of range, and Marconi was the man who figured it out and turned a toy into a powerful technology that changed the world. Before he had turned twenty years old, he had already built a device that clicked every time lightening would discharge in the vicinity of his parents' house. By the time he was twenty-one, he demonstrated his latest adaptation to his father. From across the room, Marconi could make a bell ring and do it, quite literally, out of thin air. Upon seeing this his father emptied his pockets of cash and gave it all to his son. Of course, it was going to take substantially more to make this into a practical device and eventually a weapon.

By the time that Fisher traveled to Germany and had his meetings with the Kriegsmarine, the British had already equipped the HMS Mercury with a single transmitter. This ship was an older, second line, light cruiser that operated out of Portsmouth and had been given a single job. Mercury was past her days of slugging it out with even ships of her own class. Her armor was substandard, and her design did not incorporate some of the latest features that made modern cruisers so deadly, that mostly being compartmentalization beneath her decks. What made Mercury uniquely suited for this job was actually one of her obsolete features and it was also one that had been scheduled to be removed. Despite having been built with boilers and a steam driven engine, Mercury was built with masts for sails. Fisher had the modifications canceled, and the ship's main mast became the tower for her antenna.

Mercury sailed from Portsmouth with orders not to engage the enemy. She could still build up sufficient speed to outrun most ships that would pay her any attention, but her real defense lay in her obsolescence. No cruiser or battleship were likely to attack her because sinking her would be more trouble than it was worth. The French fleet, operating out of Brest, ignored Mercury, and it would prove to be to their own peril. The French would never guess that Mercury was the real reason they were starting to lose ships for, what appeared to them to be, nothing more than bad luck.

In the first three months of Mercury's mission, the British had managed to isolate and sink a French cruiser, a destroyer, and two coastal gun boats. The French never caught on to the real source of the danger, and while this did not represent a significant threat to their fleet at large, it did force the French to rethink their operations. As a result, they became far less aggressive in the Channel. This gave the Royal Navy some much needed breathing room.

Another irony was that most British officials were just as clueless as their French counterparts. It was fortunate for the British that only one man needed to be impressed, and he was the man that originated the operation in the first place,

Jackie Fisher. He wasted no time in formulating and expanding his program. Mercury was simply a test and now he needed to upgrade his lightening detectors and make them a standard for the Royal Navy.

It was far more challenging than it sounded. Strangely enough, the problems encountered by the British were not so much on the material side since they had what they needed to build as many sets as were required. The problems were one of having trained labor to build them. There was also the equally challenging problem of training technicians to operate the sets once they were built. There was no way to get around the time required to develop the human factor into a viable resource. Fisher went full steam on the project anyway.

There were technical challenges, however. This was mostly due to the unreliability of any new technology. It was also the primary reason that the radio was limited to the navy. Despite the perceptions of weaknesses in the designs of the early sets, it is now believed that most of the breakdowns were due to the inexperience of the operators who had very little understanding of the technology and even electricity. This compounded the problem of rushed training under the pressures of war.

Even if human error was a major factor, these early sets were still delicate technology. They had a very limited range and were highly vulnerable to mother nature. Storms, which are very common at sea, rendered them almost useless. There were also other natural factors that interfered with their effectiveness and, at that time, were not fully understood. The single biggest of these was the normal activity of the sun and its own radio discharges. It would be years before anyone in the radio field would figure out what was causing these unexplained breakdowns, let alone, shielding the receivers from it.

Despite all of these problems, the radios did not have to work perfectly. They only had to work well enough. When Fisher learned of the Zeppelins, he had inadvertently discovered a way to make his radio work even better, even if at the time he had no idea that was the case. It would soon be discovered that by raising the point of transmission high into the air you got a far better range out of your set. It was only an added benefit though.

While Tirpitz might have been mostly unclear on exactly what this new technology was, he had no problem understanding the implications of putting these lightening detectors on his flying trains. It was not a popular notion with men like Schlieffen who wanted to only drop bombs from the Zeppelins. By putting radio sets on the new air fleet, it seemed to some as if the airships were simply coming full circle and were now little more than super expensive observation balloons. This argument did not dissuade Tirpitz, who also pointed out that there was no reason the Zeppelins could not have bombs and radios.

Still, what was obvious to Tirpitz, and something Schlieffen was entirely unwilling to admit, was the fact that the Zeppelin bombing attacks had failed to produce any viable results on land. It was most certainly not enough to justify continuing the program. Even the Confederate attack on Cincinnati had yielded no significant results. Tirpitz made his case, personally, to the Kaiser.

314

The most powerful weapon that could be wielded from the air were not bombs nor soldiers, it was information. The best place to use this weapon was in the one theater where information was always lacking and at a premium.

This place was the domain of Tirpitz. He wanted his new air fleet to ride a new kind of wave, much as the old fleet did those of the sea. Powered flight made balloon technology useful to fleets at sea. Not only could they attack from above, but more importantly, just like with the HMS Mercury, they could report on the enemies' movements, and in effect speed up the reaction times of friendly vessels. The limiting factor with such technology, until now, was that towing balloons from a ship was not practical. The Zeppelins did not need such a thing. With the radios, they could also scout out ahead of formations and even perform independent actions of their own.

The plan sounded good. Unfortunately, the implementation would prove to be a bit more problematic; however, just like with the radios, the system did not have to work perfectly. It only had to work well enough. The only obstacle left that Tirpitz and Fisher had in their path was a situation that would allow them to force a major naval action. Not only were their own respective governments unwilling to do such a thing, but their enemies were also not so eager. As long as that was the case, then the major fleets of the world would sit safely in their protective harbors. Luckily for the allies though, a situation was brewing in the Balkans that would eventually give Tirpitz exactly what he wanted.

A Confederate Lake

By the late summer of 1900, some were beginning to speculate that the war was thankfully drawing to a close. This was largely conjecture and being spouted in the opinion columns of any number of contemporary periodicals. What none of these opines seemed to take into consideration was that their enemies were predicting victory as much as they were. What all of these writers seemed to be detecting, both Allied and Entente, was that the war had indeed taken a few turns that left everyone in a precarious situation. They simply chose to see this situation as an opportunity for victory.

Strangely enough, only two prominent writers managed to see the situation for what it really was, and both of these men were known more for their fiction than their fact. One was an American and the other British. They were both as much novelist as they were journalist and judging by their opines, they both called the situation correctly and pointed out the dangers. The first, the American, was better known by his pen name of Mark Twain. His real name was Samuel Clemens, and for the entirety of the war he wrote for a San Francisco newspaper, but also contributed to the growing wire service of the time. The British author was later known as one of the founders of science fiction, and his name was George Orwell.

Both of these men did not so much warn of the dangers that their respective nations faced, but instead they felt that the reality was that no one was in danger because no one could really win this conflict. Clemens had more of a commonsense approach when he likened the war to a corral full of mules who all decided to have a kicking contest. His predicted outcome was, "And by the end of it all, what you got is a stable full of bruised asses".

Orwell was more technical in his evaluations and here was where he showed his true genius. Unfortunately, no one was listening to him and he quickly earned the reputation of a "nay sayer". Despite his unpopularity, he had something that so few other newspaper men did. Orwell had a clarity of vision when it came to the employment of new weapon systems, even if he had no military background. He was self-taught on the subject. He voraciously corresponded with those who did have the proper backgrounds, and Orwell had the ability to digest this information and draw a clear picture of their inevitable results. He was one of the few journalists in England that called the German bombing attacks on France as nothing more than, "Pins making pricks on a cushion". He was not as taken or horrified with these new wonder weapons that so many in his profession were.

Orwell did not see these weapons as useless; he did state that "Air supremacy will be crucial in the days and century to come". What he was really questioning was their employment, and in that at least there were many who silently agreed with him and a few of those voices counted. Among those men were Admirals Fisher and Tirpitz, both of whom were becoming, more and more as the war went on, the de facto leaders of their national navies. Unlike Orwell, or Clemens for that matter, the Admirals did see a possible opening for victory, and they saw it coming before the rapidly approaching turn of the century.

While Tirpitz enjoyed the full support of his emperor, that he had made very happy with the headlines that were being grabbed by Germany's new air fleet, Fisher was in a somewhat more precarious situation. Not only did he lack the support of some key fellow admirals, he was also squarely at odds with the Cabinet, and in particular with Chamberlain and Balfour, who were for all practical purposes running Great Britain at this point. These two key officials, who were acting in the name of Lord Salisbury, were following the recommendations of General Wolseley, no matter how gloomy those predictions might be. Their approach to the war was very conservative, while Fisher argued that in order to win they would have to take chances. This included committing elements of the home fleet to theaters abroad. The Cabinet would have none of that and routinely got in the habit of ignoring even the most mundane memos coming from Plymouth and specifically the office of the Second Lord of the Admiralty.

Despite this handicap, Fisher still had a great deal of leeway in the execution of his office, and he had wasted no time in consolidating his authority. He had removed many officers who refused to follow his lead and replaced them with like minded reformers, many of whom had a few radical ideas of their own. Fisher had a few other cards to play and he used them well. These were his allies, all of whom had assets to bring to the table and were far more eager than the Royal Navy to try new things.

Fisher and Tirpitz had developed a very smooth-running partnership since they first met in the spring. This would lead Tirpitz to suggest to Fisher that the British Admiral take a page out of the playbook of a certain British General, of whom Tirpitz had also come to know from their joint venture to southern Africa. This was Lord Horatio Kitchener, now Commander of Forces Middle East. This suggestion led to another partnership that Fisher developed, because what he could not get out of his own Cabinet he could easily get from the navy of the Confederate States of America.

The death of the Confederate Secretary Bulloch was somewhat discouraging to Fisher at first; however, it proved to be a blessing in disguise. While there was much political turmoil over who would replace Bulloch, the Confederate Navy was still steaming right along under the competent direction of their First Admiral, a man by the name of John Mercer Brooke. Admiral Brooke had been around Mobile as long as Bulloch had been in Richmond, and while Brooke was aging and almost ready to retire he was one of the many technological progressives that Bulloch kept around precisely for that very reason.

Many in Richmond considered

Brooke to be nothing more than Bulloch's former yes man. There is some truth to that view even if Brooke was a more than competent administrator in his own right. While he was temporarily the de facto leader of the entire department of the navy, he also managed to step out of Bulloch's shadow and make some decisions of his own with little to no interference from Richmond.

Despite having spent most of his later career under the coat tails of Bulloch, Brooke was no stranger to the world of politics. He preferred dealing with machines as opposed to people, but interestingly enough his first love had a lot to do with his political entanglements. Much of that had to do with him shielding his "wizards and warlocks" from the almost constant medaling of Confederate politicians who distrusted new technology almost as much as they did their black sailors. One of the most prominent of these wiz kids was none other than Astin Greene.

Brooke was primarily an engineer above all else. His way of thinking was precisely the kind of thing that Bulloch had looked for and staffed the navy with.

That made Brooke something of a shoe-in for the top seat in Mobile. Brooke was instrumental in the laying of the transatlantic telegraph cables between England and the CSA. He was also a well-known oceanographer and maritime scientist who was known in his field on both sides of the Atlantic.

Fortunately for Admiral Fisher, this gave Brooke the contacts that had formulated any number of close ties with many high officers in the Royal Navy. He also knew William Preece very well, as the two men had worked closely together on the trans-Atlantic telegraphs. In 1900, the two admirals were only professionally aware of each other and had only met briefly on a few occasions. This would rapidly change over the course of the summer of that year.

By this time, the Mexican/Confederate offensive into New Mexico was in full gear and looked to be making spectacular progress. It seemed as if the US troops were being pushed north at a rapid pace. This meant that Richmond gave Mobile the green light on executing the second phase of their grand strategy. Everything appeared to be ready.

It has to be noted that this plan must have seemed only logical to the war planners at Mechanics Hall in Richmond. When looking at it from their point of view, it does seem to make perfect sense. The Confederate war planners knew the facts and figures, and in no way could you juggle them around in order to spin the data into victory. There was simply no possibility that the CSA could defeat the USA in a large scale, protracted war. Even with the Confederacy's allies, the numbers were simply too much in favor of the US. The Confederates realized that the only way they could win was the exact same way they did the first time around. They had to create and exploit political turmoil in the US. In the summer of 1900, they did have some cause to be optimistic.

After an exchange of many telegrams, both Brooke and Fisher agreed that there were now only two vital factors that would lead to victory. The first was stopping the Russians in the Balkans, and the second was the defeat of Elihu Root in the US presidential election. Strangely enough this made two cities with absolutely nothing in common, the two most important cities on planet Earth. The first was Constantinople in Thrace. The second was Albuquerque in New Mexico. If the allies could take the latter and hold the former, then the Entente would collapse, and the Allies would hold together. If the opposite side of the coin came up then the reverse was likely true.

Fisher saw that he was in a position to do something about this situation, and Brooke, along with Tirpitz and Kitchener, became willing accomplices. They were all more than ready to bet big. This very thing was one of the decision points that Wolseley had warned the cabinet about. It is ironic that Wolseley himself did not see this developing situation for what it was. He was in complete agreement with Balfour on the matter. Both men thought that Roberts and Waldersee had the situation on the continent well in hand, and, as a result they were unwilling to risk even a small portion of the Royal Navy.

Brooke was under no such restrictions. He already had a major naval offensive prepared to go. This might have presented something of a problem once he agreed to cooperate fully with Fisher, however, it actually worked to Brooke's advantage in several ways. The first reason was simply because the CSN operation had been in the planning stages since well before Bulloch's death. No one was likely to stop it for that reason alone. There was also the added benefit that President Wheeler wanted some more quick and easy victories of the kind that Operation Grand Tour was likely to produce.

There were only a few operational details that needed to be changed in order for Brooke to provide Fisher with the required aid. Most of these went unnoticed by enemy spies who had already determined that this operation was coming as well as deducing the likely targets of the CSN. We now know that US spies never even noticed the changes in the orders of some of the Confederate ships, or some of the new equipment that was being loaded on transports. Brooke had managed to successfully keep a lid on his true intentions, and oddly enough it was more to keep his own superiors in the dark than his actual enemies.

It was mid-July when Brooke was ready to unleash his newest weapon, the

CSS Texas. She was at the core of a task force that consisted of two battleships, six cruisers, fourteen destroyers, and a host of non-capital ships that included everything from armed flotilla vessels to fleet service ships, along with what they were guarding which were transports of every type that were currently in the Confederate Merchant Service. These transports were mostly filled with troops of the CSMC and state troops from Florida, Louisiana, and even a few from Texas. The reason that these particular units were chosen for this mission was the fact that most of these units had been recruited from Latino and Cajun communities within the CSA, and all of them had a large number of Spanish and Creole speaking troops.

This fact was not something that had been overlooked by US military intelligence. They had assumed the Confederate objective was Cuba; however, the task force of Grand Tour did not steam from its bases to Havana nor even Santiago. Instead, Grand Tour dropped anchor just off the administrative capital of the French Protectorate, Martinique. St. Pierre and the islands largest city of Fort De France had been used extensively by French cruisers as supply bases for most of the war.

Occasionally, ships of the Royal Navy would sail to the island, lob some shells at the main base, and then retreat. Past that, life in Martinique went on as if there was no war at all. Manufactured goods had become extremely difficult to obtain on most of the Caribbean Islands, but these had never been readily obtainable anyway, so very little had changed. As it turned out, life under the CSA would actually improve for many of the islands' residents most of whom were ironically black.

The fighting on Martinique was short and less than furious. The French had installed some shore batteries to protect their supply base, but these half measures proved to be too few and completely inadequate. Most of them failed to fire a single shell. The invaders destroyed them before their crews could reach the positions. Confederate Marines managed to land completely unopposed on three separate shorelines, and the only ground fighting took place just outside of St. Pierre where the small garrison found itself overwhelmed. It was over in an hour and the French were forced to strike their colors. The entire island would be surrendered three days later.

This began the island-hopping campaign that would move from south to north along the chain of islands that had formerly been almost exclusively European colonies, about half of which would change their flags from the French tricolor to the Stars and Bars. The presence of CS troops that spoke Creole, Acadian, and French all helped in dealing with the local civilians. The presence of black sailors also helped. It showed the degree of meticulous planning that the CSN had put into what was the largest operation in their history. Not only were the former French colonies now receiving the benefit of a short supply chain that could provide goods and services, but they saw many of these invaders as liberators. It was clear from the early results that the campaign was getting off to a good start.

In a few years, the Gulf of Mexico would become a major headache for the Confederacy. The local populations would eventually become restless, and many ongoing insurgencies would not only continue, but flourish. There were also natural disasters that would take their toll. Two years later, a volcano would erupt on Martinique and completely destroy the Confederate Naval station along with killing every single human at the base and city, save one man. This would come on the heels of another natural disaster that would do even more damage in Texas.

The rest of the fighting would also not go as easy as it had in Martinique. Guadeloupe, the island that held the second largest French supply base, would not fall so easily. While the Confederates were able to quickly seize the important points on the island, a small band of French sailors, naval infantry, some local militia, along with a company of Foreign Legionnaires, fell back into the hills where it would take months of hard fighting before the Confederates were able to finally root them all out. This fighting would prove to be some of the most vicious and personal of the war. The fact that very few prisoners were taken, by either side, speaks volumes to that.

Despite the problems that would

come, and were quite unforeseeable in 1900, it was quite a coup for the allies. The French cruisers and their support vessels did not attempt to oppose the Confederate task force. They were under orders to operate in the area for as long as they could before retreating to the west coast of Africa. That is exactly what they did, and when it was finally clear to the allies that this had happened, they moved on their final objectives. The Confederates steamed the main part of their task force to Santiago, Cuba, where they anchored right next to the Spanish squadron stationed there. The smaller portion of their task force centered around the battleship Shenandoah, peacefully put in at San Juan, Puerto Rico. In both cases, the CSA peacefully took possession of both islands from Spain. This would be the last peaceful thing to happen on either island for some time to come.

For the time being, in a cheap and quick campaign, the CSN had turned the Gulf of Mexico into what Joseph Wheeler would go on to call, "a Confederate Lake". It all but ended US ambitions of building a canal in northern Columbia, or at least for the time being. Strangely enough one of the more important results of the campaign was not known at the time and it had little to do with Confederate operations.

Using the shock and confusion caused by the Confederate offensive, the Royal Navy saw an opportunity to carry out a few of their own plans that, up until that point, they had simply lacked the resources to do. With the French raiders finally out of the region, several British ships were freed up to carry out their own strike on an island that the CSA had very little interest in. Ironically enough, this plan had been drawn up by none other than Jackie Fisher while he commanded the Caribbean Naval Squadron.

The target of the Royal Navy was a small and unremarkable island off the coast of French Guiana. Nothing was there but a controversial prison that was appropriately known as Devil's Island. It was militarily insignificant, but Fisher had recognized that there was at least one thing of value there. British sailors occupied the island, and the French authorities not only failed to resist, but actually ran to the British for protection as their prisoners had revolted on them several days earlier. The British had to actually fight some of the very men they would later set free.

Since President Boulanger had come to power, he had stocked the prison with any number of political opponents. These men were more than eager to help the British in weakening the French Government. Some of them would later prove to be useful, but they were also not the main target of the raid. The British were only interested in one man on the island. He was the subject of a witch hunt that had resulted from the exposure of a spy ring in French Counterintelligence.

The real culprit of this spy ring was Ferdinand Esterhazy. He had been the same man that was providing Field Marshall Waldersee with information that allowed the German general to see the war that was coming. Esterhazy was now living free, in neutral Switzerland, where he had moved once he mustered out of the French Army. The man was living off the funds he was paid as a German spy.

The man that had been blamed for Esterhazy's crimes suddenly found himself a guest of the Royal Navy, and he was eager to cooperate in bringing down the French dictator. This man had been the subject of a worldwide media storm when his trial took place. He was still well known in France, where many thought that he was railroaded because he happened to be a Jew. There was a great deal of truth to this belief even if it was far more complicated than just simple ethnic prejudices. Alfred Dreyfus was the man's name, and he would eventually become a central figure in the movement to overthrow Boulanger.

The Oriental Not So Express

General Alexander Fok had spent the earlier part of the war in the far eastern region of the Russian Empire. He had also served in Manchuria and eventually Korea, where he commanded the Sixth Siberian Rifles. So far, the Russo-American army had fought the Japanese to a standstill just south of the Yalu River. With the presence of the American fleet at Port Arthur, the British were having a hard time providing the Japanese army with everything they needed on the peninsula. It limited the size and scope of Japanese operations, and,as such they never could build up a large enough presence to overwhelm Entente forces.

Back in St. Petersburg, Emperor Nicholas did not quite see the American Navy as the principle author of victory in Korea. He did not seem to even understand that what had been achieved there was not even a victory, but rather just one more stalemate. No matter the military situation, the stalemate was all that was required to allow continued domination of the Chinese Emperor Gangxhu, and by extension the Russian control of Manchuria along with American dominance in Northern China. It was victory enough for Nicholas.

It was also a sideshow and Nicholas did seem to grasp this much. He at least understood that victory in the overall war would greatly depend on the outcome of the campaign in the Balkans. Nicholas reasoned that since his forces had done so well in the east, then an Eastern General should command his troops on the southern front. That was how Fok was promoted and posted to Bucharest, where he was given overall command of all forces in the region. The campaign had bogged down and Fok was expected to get things moving again.

Fok was not met with a total disaster nor were his prospects bleak. The Balkans had not degenerated into an elongated siege line as had all of the other fronts. There was still room to maneuver and the Russian Army still had most of their potential foes outnumbered and gunned. There was also a larger plan at work that involved Russia's principle allies in the theater, those being Italy and France. If the overall strategy succeeded, then Constantinople would fall. This would allow the naval power of Russia to combine with those of France and Italy. Britain could not possibly hope to hold that back, and the entire Mediterranean would belong to the Entente. Fok had good reason to be optimistic.

When Italy found itself at war with the wrong side they did not seem to take very long to be confused about what had happened on the diplomatic front. Many in the kingdom realized that it did not really matter. They only needed to be in the war to carry out their goals and the side they were on was only a technicality. The Italians wasted no time changing their war plans to fit the new situation, and quickly launched an attack on Trieste in the Austrian Hungarian Empire. It was a disaster.

The Austrians mauled some of Italy's best troops. Soon Trieste was reinforced with not just other units from the Hapsburg empire, but also a flood of fresh German conscripts and some of the reserve divisions from Alsace Lorraine. Given the terrain on the Austro-Italian border, the fighting quickly bogged down and both sides seemed content to leave the front be.

It still forced Italy to do something they had not really wished to do and would be unpopular for the entire war. They had to invite French troops into Italy in order to help defend their northern border. A few months later a French Army would also be occupying southern Italy near ports where they awaited transport across the Ionian Sea. The plan was to move this army along with large numbers of Italian soldiers to Albania. Once there, they could move inland and link up with Fok's Russian army. Nothing that the allies had in the region would be able to stop them. Constantinople would fall.

The allies were not unaware of the danger they faced. They were also very aware of the other problem that an Entente landing in Albania would bring about. Greece had remained on the sidelines, so far. This was not a sign of peaceful intentions and everyone knew it. The Greeks were itching for an excuse to go to war with Turkey. The only thing holding them back was the stalemate just north of their border in Serbia. If the Entente, also at war with Turkey, could gain the upper hand then there would be very little to hold back the Greeks.

The situation was already so close that anything could tip the scales including the very small Greek military. Still, this was not the primary concern of Kitchener in Egypt. If Greece joined the Entente, then their ports and railroads that led directly to the front would become available to the French and Italians. This would give them a vastly superior position compared to Albania, where they would have to use roads that barely deserved the name.

Once Tirpitz returned to Egypt to command the naval part of allied operations, both he and Kitchener were in complete agreement. If they reacted to the enemy moves, then they would lose. That left them with only one choice, and this was to go over on the offensive. The allies would have to seize Albania first. Roberts, who was still stalled in front of Belgrade, would have to get around the city somehow. The reality of the situation was that the allies would need to be the ones who linked up first. This would turn the tables on the situation. There was only one monumental problem standing in the way. It was the Italian Navy.

Of Rifles And Men

It seemed to Lord Roberts that the fighting just outside of Belgrade was a case of an irresistible force meeting an unmovable object. Indeed, this seemed to be an apt description for the entire war. By the end of the second year of the conflict, some of the conditions that were responsible for the quagmire were slowly starting to change. Some of them for the better and others for the worse. There were many who did not recognize this basic fact, and unfortunately for the men in the trenches their military leaders were among that number.

What too many generals, politicians, and war planners had failed to recognize from the very start of the conflict was the caliber of solider they were commanding and fighting. These men were too busy counting the caliber of their guns. It seems to have been an odd side effect of the prevailing thinking that dominated the pre-war era. Science was the big game in town and applying this method of thinking to everything was the big sport of the day. The militaries of the world had gladly embraced this, and it would take a new generation to temperate this completely mathematical approach to war.

This is not to say that math is wrong or useless. As the statisticians of that day correctly pointed out, numbers are numbers and they are inherently neutral. What they completely failed to grasp was that an equation will not adequately simulate reality if you lack some of the variables. In real world terms, this means that how many rounds a man can fire in a minute is irrelevant if he does not, or cannot, achieve that task. This was never clearer than in the case of the lever action battle rifles that were produced by the United States and Russia.

Lord Roberts had given up on frontal assaults on Belgrade after the first several attempts had failed to produce any positive gains. He then chose the tactic that is often favored by military men when they believe that a forward approach has failed, the flanking maneuver. More often than not, the attempt to go around enemy fire is an excuse for failure and an admission of not knowing what to do next. That is not to say that flanking is not an invaluable tactic, it most certainly is as the Roman Legions first proved, but if done in an act of desperation it is anything but. This seems to be the case with Robert's attempts to cut Belgrade off from its vital southern rail line that connected it to its Russian supply base.

General Fok had sent reinforcements to Belgrade as well as

supplies, but politics got in the way of the Russian troops actively participating in the defense of the city. General Milan, who was not only running the war, had now taken de facto control of the entire Serbian Government and was reluctant to allow the Russians to actively participate in the city's defense. Milan had his own problems of an internal nature in dealing with the radical patriots who were being directly financed by the Russians.

Milan was not stupid. He realized that having Russian troops in the city would make Serbia little more than a very poor province of the Russian Empire. If he let the Russians in, then he would have to fight two wars. The first one against the allies, and then a second war to get the Russians out after the bigger one was complete. This would effectively destroy Serbia permanently, so the best way to handle the problem was to keep it from happening in the first place. In this struggle at least, time was on Milan's side.

The Serbian General and former King seemed to have been one of the few military leaders who understood the human equation. The Black Hand, the Serbian radicals, were doing more than their fair share of fighting. As a result of this they were also taking more than their fair share of casualties. Milan realized that by thinning out the herd he was only strengthening his own hand in the post war world. Milan might have cooperated with these radicals. He might have even sympathized with their cause to a degree, but he was not one of them and was well aware they could not afford to keep him around after the war.

This political situation created a new set of problems for Entente forces in the region. Milan was also slowly losing his ability to defend the city. It might eventually come down to allowing Russians in the city proper. As Roberts moved to the south and west of Belgrade, it was something of a breath of fresh air for Milan. It took direct pressure off his lines and forced the Russian reserve, camped well south of Belgrade, into action on a front that no one could deny was becoming critical.

We know a great deal about this action because of a particular individual involved. Winston Churchill had since left Kitchener's army and had returned to England. He had the opportunity to take a seat in Parliament upon his return, but instead he chose to stay with the army when he learned it was deploying to the continent. He was no longer acting in his official capacity as a reporter even if he did write a number of articles while serving. He also wrote extensively in his journals about this front and this operation in particular. Churchill, at the tender young age of 25 found himself leading an entire battalion of infantry, and it was spearheading the flanking maneuver around the Serbian lines.

Initially, Churchill's battalion met very little resistance. When the Russians finally showed up in force the British had the advantage of picking their own ground, and Churchill's men dug in along a small series of ridge lines just south of the village of Sabac. They had plenty of warning about the advancing Russian infantry and were prepared for an assault. What happened in the initial engagements fully illustrates the monumental importance of the caliber of men over the caliber of guns. It also demonstrated the first serious crack in the national defense systems of the time and how critical this problem was going to get, despite the fact that no one at the time seemed to have noticed.

Men like Churchill, all along the front lines of the world, certainly did even though no one was listening to them. Churchill wrote that his men were on edge about facing the Russian infantry. At this point in the war the Russians were enjoying a reputation of near invincibility despite having never really earned this. To venture an opinion, I believe this had a great deal to do with the fact that they had been so seriously underestimated before the war, and when they fought with equal tenacity and skill it was quite a shock to their opponents. Each view of the Russian fighting skill was unrealistic and both views seemed to be rooted in racist stereotypes of the time.

The truth of the matter was that the Russians had good, mediocre, and bad troops just like any other army. The sheer size of their army, the luck of the draw, and their national war plans had a lot to do with creating one myth after another. Their Generals seemed to be as prone to believing these myths as anyone else, and as is human nature they picked and chose the ones they actually believed.

Fok most certainly was under some serious misconceptions about the abilities of the troops he now commanded in the west. Like many men who found themselves elevated in command, due to the war, he had been running a smaller formation of elite troops for years before the conflict and had failed to understand that the larger forces that he now led were not the same. Part of the problem was simple aesthetics. Just because a man puts on a uniform and can be taught to stay in step with others does not make him a professional soldier. Neither does the weapon he carries, and in the case of the Russians this would prove to be a serious flaw.

If the Russian military had outperformed its expectations, Russian industry did them one better. The Russians were turning out American battle rifles and French rapid fire seventy-five-millimeter artillery pieces from their own factories. These factories had been set up by their allies, but by this time they were being largely managed by Russians. They managed to turn out huge sums of weapons and the ammunition to go with them. They produced so much, in fact, that the Russians were equipping nearly every unit they had with these weapons which had proven to be so effective around Warsaw.

The problem was that the troops facing the Germans, in central Poland, were mostly pre-war regular soldiers. They had received more than adequate training on what were the most high-tech weapons on the battlefield. As these men were slowly being killed off, their replacements were receiving less training and had almost no practical experience. Fok's soldiers were in even worse shape in that many had been conscripted and had as little as a few weeks training before they were deployed. While working a lever that loaded bullets might seem simple to many of us today, that has a great deal to do with the fact that we have the benefit of war movies, books, magazines, and the fact that this technology is now over a century old.

The British troops that encountered the first waves of the Russian attack slaughtered entire regiments of troops that simply vanished in a hail of fire. Churchill's comments about what his scouts found after the fighting was very telling. They recovered many Russian copies of the Winchester battle rifles. Nearly one in three had never been loaded, while even the ones that had ammunition in their magazines had not been fired. Churchill described enemy artillery fire as having been "weak and wildly inaccurate."

The Winchester and the Colt Battle rifles had performed well enough in the hands of American, Boer, and the regular troops of the Russian Army. These weapons had initially been used in the fighting in Missouri some three decades before the war. The weapons of this war were some four generations removed from the prototypes and had many changes from the earlier weapons. Despite the improvements, some of the serious flaws in the weapons had not been rooted out by 1900.

Most of these flaws were taken care of by adequate training and good sergeants. The rifles were made with a high degree of precision that would cause a German clock maker to be envious. While this might sound like a good thing and, from an engineering standpoint it does show true craftsmanship, but it was not a desirable quality in field service.

Taking the weapon apart to clean it in battlefield conditions was difficult. Putting it back together was even more so and this rifle required that a soldier do that almost constantly and all of this had to be done in a muddy trench.

The other serious flaw was not so much in the weapon itself. The entire concept behind it was just simply too ahead of its time. Conventional thinking of the day was leaning towards the ability of the average foot soldier to shoot accurately at a much further range. Sights on more conventional bolt action rifles speak volumes to this. The flip up sights on most could be adjusted for targets out to 1100 meters. With the exception of a few specialty rifles, the American weapons had fixed sights and were generally only accurate out to 500 meters. These weapons were designed to produce large volumes of fire over accuracy.

Unfortunately, the US Army, the main advocate of their rather unique small arm, completely ignored their engineers and theoreticians who would later be proven correct. At the start of the war, the US Army was still stressing exactly what everyone else was, long range accuracy over high volumes of fire. After a few firefights, American troops would learn to ignore their training and began spitting out as much lead as they could, but due to the deficiencies in their training it would take them a while to develop tactics that complimented this ability. As of 1900, none had yet to appear.

These problems were only compounded by the problems faced in the Russian Army. The average American was at least somewhat familiar with the concepts that went into their battle rifles. Most Russians, particularly those from rural areas, were not. Many of their conscripts had never held a rifle in their life. A good number of them had never even seen one. Of those that had, the weapons they were familiar with ranged from muzzle loading weapons still used for hunting in Russia, to simple target rifles that had to be loaded one round at a time. Neither of these looked or functioned anything like the American weapons that they were now being thrown into war with.

Many Russians would die because

they had no idea that the box that was mounted underneath the chamber was a magazine for holding ammunition. Churchill's men found weapons that had cigarettes stored there. Some weapons that had been fired were obviously manually fed because the packing cloth was still in the magazine well. This was despite the fact that the dead Russian soldiers were all fully loaded down with ammunition in their pouches and pockets. In fact, it seemed as if they had more ammunition than their British enemies. An obvious case where simple numbers did them no good at all.

Due to the inequality of the soldiers and the lack of attention paid to this fact by the Generals commanding them, the British were able to successfully threaten the supply lines that fed Belgrade. It was certainly not the only factor that Milan was facing, but it would soon become a critical one. He would slowly begin evacuating the city with plans to fall back on Skopje in upper Macedonia. Milan delayed this for as long as he could because he understood the political consequences. From that location he would be completely sub-servant to Fok and the Russians. It was a political nightmare, but militarily speaking the day when he had no choice in the matter was rapidly approaching.

The Ionian Sea

Operations at the mouth of the Adriatic, in late August of 1900, never became a headline event in the newspapers, and as a result it was never labeled with a name such as the Battle of the Yellow Sea. One can easily surmise that the area was already important and highly contested before the Balkan situation made it a primary theater. Austria-Hungary had already found itself in something of a crisis when Italy joined the war and threatened to cut off the Adriatic shipping. Not only did this increase the tempo of naval operations, but several formerly unimportant areas suddenly became critical, and Austrian and German troops marched into, and occupied neutral Montenegro.

There was no major stand up fight between major fleets in the Ionian Sea. Newspapers usually make their money by printing exceptions, and in 1900 such a battle would have been just that. That is still unfair not to call the Ionian operations anything but a battle. It was simply overlooked by the press, because for the time it was not what people thought of as noteworthy. Ironically, the operations in the area would be a forerunner for what would be major naval operations in the future. Still, how can you not call it a battle since the capital ships of six nations were deployed to the area and ultimately involved in the fighting. The only real difference between the Yellow and Ionian seas were that, in the latter, they simply clashed in a piecemeal fashion and not all at once.

Historians still argue over which operations began and ended this particular "battle." I tend to group the operations of the last three weeks of August as what constitutes the bulk of important moves that were taken in the Ionian Sea. These are the operations that were specifically in support of both sides' attempts to occupy Albania. I have thought that the natural starting point was the redeployment of French Admiral Ernest Fournier's main task force in early August. This included two of France's primary battleships of the Charles Martel class that were considered so important that, when they were built, they prompted debate in the English Parliament.

Unfortunately for France, by 1900 most of their capital ships were well past their prime and not considered overly effective against the Royal Sovereigns of Great Britain. The introduction of the CSS Texas would render most of the France's major warships, if not every battleship on the planet, obsolete. Still, in August of that year they were powerful enough for what France required, and that was particularly true when you consider that they were working in conjunction with the Italian Navy.

Many jokes have been made about Italy and, in particular, her navy. While this might be the usual fodder of coffee shops and armchair admirals, the fact is that war room planners did not have the luxury of writing the Italians off. This was very true in 1900 when Italy was in possession of one of the newest and most modern fleets in existence. Compared to that of the Royal Navy, it was very small, but on a ship to ship basis the Italian vessels were clearly superior to anything the British could send against them. As with France, Italy had her share of modern cruisers that were built for the same purposes. In the realm of capital vessels, Italy also had two vessels that had concerned the British for some time, those being the battleships, Caio Dullio and Enrico Dandolo. Their appearance in the late seventies had even prompted the British to copy their designs with the building of the HMS Inflexible.

Interesting to note that the Inflexible had been originally commanded by one of the architects of this battle, Jackie Fisher. It is even more important to note that while both Italian ships were still in active service at the time and the core of the Regia Maria. At the same time, the Inflexible had already been relegated to the reserve fleet and guard duty at Portsmouth. Even so, both Dullio and Dandolo had been upgraded several times since their first trials, and ironically many of their improvements came directly from Britain. Their limitations had yet to be truly discovered until the Ionian Sea. In August of 1900, they were still of serious concern to the British Royal Navy.

Franco-Italian operations, also had one serious advantage over allied efforts. It was an advantage that was as simple as geography. Entente forces were primarily operating out of the Italian base at Taranto and were very close to their ultimate objective, Albania. Allied forces had several bases in the area including both Malta and the Austrian bases in the Adriatic, but the bulk of their forces had to operate out of Alexandria in Egypt. This advantage might have assured the Entente a victory had Tirpitz not turned their ultimate trump card into a liability by introducing what would come to dominate naval operations for a century.

It was not long after the first French ships dropped anchor in the well defended harbor of Taranto that they discovered their defenses had suddenly been completely negated by Germany's new wonder weapons. Smaller Austrian airships had already been over flying Taranto for weeks, watching for the inevitable arrival of French warships. For this reason, the Italian defenses paid little mind when the first German airships appeared over the port. Entente intelligence was well aware that the German air fleet had redeployed. They had simply dismissed it as unimportant since the raids in France had proven to be largely ineffectual. They would soon change their minds.

The German air fleet never did any crippling damage with any one raid on Taranto. The first attack managed to set a few buildings on fire and none of them were critical. The damage they did to the actual port facilities at the water line was minimal and easily repaired. The Germans were far from mastering any accurate means of delivering their payloads. In order to compensate for this problem, what the Germans did do was increase the size of their ordinance. This method met with mixed results and quite possibly cost them the most critical hit that they scored in the first raid on Taranto.

LZ-36 not only managed to land a hit on the French battleship Charles Martel, but she hit the Martel with one of the large "Marineshiffkampf," or quite literally, ship killers. It was a rather fat looking, fin-stabilized bomb that was carried nose down inside the actual rigid frame of the newer class of Zeppelins. It had been specifically built to bomb

Taranto. Had the bomb detonated as planned it would have most likely blown Martel right out of the water. Fortunately for the French, ships of the time were not armored against air attacks, and the bomb crashed effortlessly thru the weather deck, above the forecastle, and continued through the vessel until it punched a hole in her bottom. The bomb buried itself in the mud below the harbor and would harmlessly detonate two days later.

Still, the Germans had made their point and their victory was more than cosmetic. The damage to Martel was repairable, but she was not going to participate in the actions of August 1900. Unfortunately for the Germans, their early success prompted an immediate reaction from the French. Ever since the Paris raid, the French military had quickly began looking for a counter to the Zeppelins, and their first stop gap measure showed some signs of success. What the French had was their new anti-aircraft guns, which were basically converted seventy-five-millimeter artillery pieces with new sights and an under carriage that allowed for maximum elevation. Taranto was a good place for a first field test since the Germans had stopped nearly all bombing in France (because of the redeployment to the Austrian coast). Now that the French had a place to send their guns, they would make Zeppelin operations expensive over Taranto, and more importantly they would greatly reduce the effects of the bombing. The Martel was the first and last ship to be hit in Taranto.

Fortunately for the allies, the bombing was never meant to be anything more than simple harassment, and in that much it was an unqualified success. It forced the Entente to change many things about their operations, and it made their safe haven feel like anything but. Tirpitz also had a secondary objective in mind when it came to his flying trains. The bombing was something of a diversion and this worked even better than the harassment objective. It was meant to deceive the French and Italian navies as to the real purpose of the Zeppelins. They had a far more powerful weapon than their bombs. The most important weapon they now carried were their British "Lightening Detector" crews.

Just like with the tests done by

HMS Mercury, Admiral Fournier never seemed to have guessed what was going on with the Zeppelins. When you read the reports of both the French Navy and the Regia Marina, it is quite obvious that they understood the Zeppelins were scouting for the allied fleet. What they most definitely never caught on to was how fast this information was reaching the various allied task forces operating in the area. The practical effect of these radio reports was that it completely negated the geographical advantage held by the Entente. It eliminated the need for time and fuel consuming patrols and gave the Royal Navy and her allies the ability to concentrate power in critical areas while the Entente forces had to remain spread out. This would translate into several victories for the allies and it appeared to Fournier to be nothing more than bad luck on his part.

Fournier also felt that as long as his capital ships were operating in the area, then the allies could not risk large troop movements from Egypt because they could not adequately protect the transports. This was very conventional thinking, and he never realized he was fighting very unconventional forces at this point. Any amphibious operations to secure Albanian ports would leave the allied fleet vulnerable, and he was simply waiting for his chance to strike with his real power. Again, Fournier seems to have been clueless as to the capabilities that this new technology was offering the allies.

The basic assumption that the Royal Navy would be exposed while protecting amphibious operations was fundamentally correct; however Fournier was quite blind as to what was going on. This was again made so by the presence of the enemy air cover which hampered reconnaissance efforts by Entente warships. The Italians had managed to lay mines in the harbor of Durazzo, which would have made even an unopposed landing hazardous and time consuming. This would have truly made the allied fleet vulnerable as they would have to sit at anchor outside the harbor and protect the effort to clear the mines. This combined with the fact that Albania offered very few places along its coast to safely land troops would have made ideal conditions for the Entente's fleet to strike and cause serious damage. Fortunately for Tirpitz, this was never required.

As Fournier waited for his opportunity, he was unaware that allied troops were already in Albania and had long since seized the port of Durazzo along with several others. This would seem almost logical since Austrian-occupied Montenegro shared a border with Albania; however the mountains and poor conditions of the roads made large scale operations of this type nearly impossible. Again, this was only if you considered the conventional capabilities of the time, and the allies were now able to get around these problems. The first allied troops to land in Durazzo did not come from the sea. They were special German infantry companies that roped in via their transports, three Zeppelins that were modified specifically for this purpose. These troops were followed by British Engineers along with Austrian Naval personnel. The port was quickly secured, and several vessels that were sitting idle in Durazzo's port were pressed into service as makeshift mine sweepers. When the first of Kitchener's troops arrived, via naval transports from Egypt the port was already serviceable, and no amphibious operations were even required.

These airborne operations were so successful that Admiral Fournier would not even be aware that they took place until after the war. When his capital ships would sortie to intercept the large convoy from Egypt, Fournier sailed for Durazzo and his plan was to sit and wait for the Royal Navy to deploy for amphibious operations. The Entente task force would never reach their objective, and this had nothing to do with the protection for the convoy. Fournier's movements were immediately detected and reported by the Zeppelins and Tirpitz then played his trump card.

Some weeks earlier, at the conclusion of the Confederate Operation Grand Tour, the task force centered on the CSS Texas dropped anchor in the harbor of Santiago De Cuba. The Spanish squadron, normally stationed there, was preparing to leave once the city was officially handed over to the Confederate States. The Spanish did as they had always planned, only when they set sail for Europe most of the Confederate task force left with them. The deception seems to have worked, and this is never clearer than when you read US Naval Intelligence reports. They did notice that the Confederate warships were gone, but never realized that the Texas and her escorts were sailing towards the Mediterranean with the Spanish. Task Force Alamo would not show up again on Entente maps, until it was encountered by Fournier in the Ionian Sea.

The engagement was far smaller than the battle of the Yellow Sea, but this battle would be far more important. The design of the Texas, supported by her modern cruiser force, would conclusively prove its worth. As Confederate Admiral Brooke would later note, "When them Italian ships were hit, they stayed hit". Of course, this particular aspect had less to do with the Texas and more to do with the fact that the Italian Navy had yet to pick up the damage control habits that had proven their worth at the battle of the Yellow Sea and were now being rapidly adopted by every other navy in the world. What can be attributed to the CSS Texas was not even her superior armament or protection, but the fact that she hit her targets far more than her opposition. Texas was very outnumbered in her slugfest, but she had the advantage of firing over the horizon, well out of range of most of the Entente's guns. The targeting information was also being observed by her German air cover and relayed via the radio sets. This allowed the Texas to stay out of range of most of the guns that could really hurt her.

Also, the Texas did not seek to force an outright battle, and at first Fournier was more than happy to oblige. It was only after the Caio Dullio was severely damaged that he felt obliged to try and force an all-out engagement with the Confederate task force. His attempts to run them off were only playing into the hands of the Confederates since their primary objective was delay. When Task Force Alamo engaged, they had never thought the battle would be so conclusive. What the Confederates did know was that slowly the primary ships of the French and Italian navies were having to sail south and east, away from the British task force that was transporting Kitchener's army.

The Zeppelins were also not just scouting either. They never managed to land a single hit on an Entente ship, but they did force the French vessels to break their formations and make time consuming maneuvers in order to avoid being lined up in a German bomb sight. This rendered much of their return fire at the CSS Texas ineffective. By the time that Fournier signaled his ships to break off and return to Taranto, the Texas had managed to hit every single capital ship in the Entente task force.

The older French Ironclad Trident was severely damaged and lagged behind the task force allowing her to be finished off by Confederate cruisers. The Magneta managed to make it back to port but would never leave Taranto. She was taking on to much water, and three days after dropping anchor a partial collapse of a bulkhead would cause severe flooding. She would have completely capsized had she not been in the shallow harbor. Even the Brennus, which was serving as Fournier's flagship, was threatened with complete destruction by fire. Her crew was eventually able to get it under control, but Brennus would still be out of service for over a year.

This was not just a blow to operations in the Ionian Sea. This would have serious ramifications to operations in the Mediterranean in general, and the ever-crucial Western Med in particular. It was also not over with as Fournier retreated to base. The Zeppelins would harass his fleet all the way back, and even the airships that had expended their ordinance would cause great concern since the sailors below had no idea this was the case. It also served to keep the Entente eyes looking up, when they had no idea that the most serious of threats was coming from an entirely different direction. The Zeppelins were also herding the Entente task force right into the trap.

The Confederates had brought more than the CSS Texas to the battle. Waiting just past the minefields that protected the approaches to the port of Taranto were seven of the newest vessels of the Confederate Navy. The Zeppelins had already seen the channels used by the French and Italians, and now they were guarded by something more lethal than mines. Seven Confederate submarines had been deployed by cruisers in the days leading up to the battle. The cruisers had delivered these boats at night, well beyond the picket ships that guarded the harbor. The subs were of a newer design and had better range and power than the prototypes used in the Chesapeake. They anchored themselves and laid in wait for the first targets that were worth exposing their position for.

Three of the submarines would not return, yet there is no record that the Italian Navy discovered or sunk them. Their fate remains a mystery to this day. None of the Confederate submarines saw Fournier's task force leave, but the return of the Entente fleet was another story. The Entente ships were hard to miss since several were leaving behind a smoke trail and Zeppelins were hovering around them like a pack of flies. One submarine, the CSS Fin, got lucky and was able to maneuver within range of her two torpedoes.

The Enrico Dandolo had, so far, escaped any serious damage and was probably the most effective capital ship left in Fournier's task force. She had actually managed to fight off a serious effort by the Confederate cruisers to scatter the task force's screening vessels so that the CS torpedo flotilla could make a run at the French battleships. The Texas never had time to seriously concentrate on Dandolo since the Italian ship never made any real attempt to engage. Unfortunately for Dandolo, this put her at the lead of the Entente retreat, and she would blunder right into the path of the CSS Fin. Both torpedos hit their mark and Dandolo rolled over, broke in half, and went down with most of her crew. This defeat, added to the near crippling damage that was already done to the Caio Dullio, would in effect take the Italian Navy right out of the war.

The effects of this battle would change the scoreboard in the Ionian Sea. Kitchener's troops would land even if they would not immediately become a threat to the Russo-Serbian Army in Macedonia. The weather and mountains would hamper Kitchener's attempts to link up with Roberts. In fact, the German attempt to supply Kitchener by Zeppelins would cost them more airships than all of the combat operations combined. Despite this setback, the effects of the allied victory cannot be understated.

The most important of these effects was that Greece elected to remain neutral. As much as the Greeks wished to resume hostilities with the Turks, they now found themselves almost completely surrounded by allied forces, and the reputation of both Kitchener, along with those of the Zeppelins was enough to cause the hawk faction inside of Greece to back down. The other effect was, in the long run, probably more important even if it did not seem so at the time. The attempt by the Entente to link up in the Balkans had now been effectively squashed. Not only did they lack the ports to do this, but their naval strength was no longer up to the task. In essence that left the French Army locked in place with nowhere to go. They had just been taken out of the war, and the last chance they had to bring their firepower to bear was lost. The French troops in Italy would have to stay there and could no longer threaten either the Balkans or Egypt.

San Acacia

The performance of the Confederate Navy in both the Caribbean and Ionian Sea made for something of a high-water mark for the CSA. These actions might have bought Joe Wheeler some goodwill with his war weary populace, but strangely enough, it only intensified the raging political firestorm that was being deliberately kept out of the newspapers and confined mostly to the inner halls of the Confederate Government. So far, in this war, the Navy had performed brilliantly. There was no blockade of the Confederate coastline as was the case in the last war. The navy had fought on both land and sea in places as far flung as Africa and Europe, while managing to secure the CSA's new possessions in the Gulf and the Pacific.

All of these victories should have been cause for mass celebration, but no one in the Confederate Government was making much of them because of the fact that the bedrock of their successful maritime ventures were their former slaves. This was at a time when their almost exclusively white army had been under performing at nearly every turn. While it is true that the army had held back the only real Yankee offensive in Tennessee, it was also true that they had lost ground while doing it and their war winning plan, something that they bragged about before the war, that of capturing Washington, had been a complete disaster.

What Wheeler needed to take the heat off of his administration was the army deliver him a solid victory. This would ease the silent calls to discharge nearly every sailor in his fleet and give him something solid to put in the newspapers and assure an uneasy public that they were winning the war. That was something sorely needed. Even if the average Confederate civilian was not at risk of starvation, the war had managed to slowly grind the economy of the CSA to a halt. It was true there was no blockade, but there really did not have to be one. The war on international shipping was doing the job of reducing imports and exports just as thoroughly. People were feeling the pinch.

That is why the New Mexican campaign was becoming almost as important to Joe Wheeler as it was to Elihu Root. Today, it is easy to look at the fighting of late summer and early fall of 1900 and dismiss it as just one more campaign amongst many. At the time, in the hearts of two nations, this campaign was quickly becoming the entire war, and it had displaced nearly every other headline. With this in mind, it is easy to understand why President Root had pinned his reelection fortunes on the outcome of this campaign and, in particular, which flag was flying over Albuquerque. He had what seemed to be a good reason to worry.

What few people outside of New Mexico remembered from the American 61 was that the state (then a territory) had not escaped the war unscathed. Not only had the Confederates invaded New Mexico, but they had managed to occupy Albuquerque and the territorial capital of Santa Fe. Had the CSA been able to send more reinforcements then it is all too likely that New Mexico would have been permanently flying the Stars and Bars. A lack of railroads and manpower had prevented this from happening, and ultimately the invaders were driven out. This fact was never far from the front of General Pershing's mind and he made reference to the 1862 campaign on more than one occasion. He also realized that his enemy now had the things that they had once lacked.

Pershing's understanding of this was somewhat ominous in that, so far, he had read the entire situation correctly. He understood what he was facing and what he had to throw in the enemy's way. This was why he maintained that a conventional defense would not work, and he could not afford to get into a static front situation. If this were to happen then attrition would quickly reduce his defenses and the US would lose New Mexico. Pershing, along with Funston, Wood, and even Roosevelt had traveled to Washington in late May and stated as much to General Shafter. They also presented their plans on exactly how this should be handled.

Much hay has been made about Bill Shafter and, in particular, his excessive three-hundred-and-fifty-pound frame. He is often portrayed as sleepy, lethargic, lazy, and sometimes even stupid. The truth is that Shafter was anything but. Not only was Shafter well read, but he was also a very practical man and he agreed with Pershing. Shafter understood the implications for New Mexico and even what it meant for the entire war effort. According to Roosevelt's writings on the meetings, Shafter completely understood that the enemy was trying to take away the initiative that the US currently enjoyed. As he saw it, losing that would be far worse than having Eugene Debbs sitting in the White House.

This was the primary reason that Pershing was ordered to hold the enemy with the meager resources that were already at his disposal. Pershing had already anticipated this situation and that was how he got Shafter to approve his basic plan. Both men understood that this plan was both dangerous and, more to the point, politically indefensible. Had General Miles been occupying Shafter's chair, it is unlikely that he would have ever approved such a plan, but Shafter was most definitely not Miles. Shafter agreed to take the political heat and allow Pershing to do what they each thought was the best thing for their country. In essence, Shafter had just agreed to stand up and take a bullet for his cause.

The political firestorm that resulted from the invasion of New Mexico brought about many calls to have General Shafter sacked and replaced. When Debbs pulled ahead of Root in the election polls, the president finally stepped in and ordered Shafter to redeploy troops from Canada to New Mexico. Shafter had been prepared for this eventuality and stuck to the plan. He knew that the key to the war was not the city of Albuquerque, but in crossing the St. Lawrence Seaway and taking Britain out of the war in North America. The US could not do both, and this was a fact that Shafter was all too aware of. Still, he could not ignore a Presidential order. Shafter obeyed those orders to the very letter.

This order stated that several divisions were to be redeployed and that is exactly what Shafter did. The flags and standards of the units in Canada were rolled up, given a small honor guard, and sent to Santa Fe where they were declared operational on the map boards in Washington. The men and regiments that had made up these units for the entire war were left in Canada and given new designations. This exercise in military semantics worked for a while, but word eventually got out and Shafter was forced to move some men. He moved only some. Shafter told his front-line commanders to ask for some "volunteers" to form a cadre for the new divisions and this small number of men were sent to New Mexico.

At the time, no one realized the impact this particular order would later have. Shafter, knowing the temperament of the average division commander, realized all too well that these "volunteers" would be the problemed children of their front line commanders. One of these men would be Captain Woodburry Cane. From a conventional standpoint, it would seem a logical move since, in theory, it would make the divisions in Canada more productive. The reality was something different, but would prove to be far more advantageous. Many of these malcontents were the officers and NCO's who had been agitating for a complete rewriting of the book of small unit tactics. Now they would all be in one place so they could compare notes and refine their experience into a realistic plan.

This would have no effect on current operations though. While Shafter waged a political war in Washington, Pershing was having to deal with the current situation with what he had. He executed these plans exactly as they had been drawn up before the invasion began. His greatly outnumbered forces would fight a series of skirmishes, designed to only slow the advance of enemy forces as they pushed up the Rio Grande river valley. US troops would never stand long enough to be drawn into a full scale pitched battle.

These 'stand and then run' tactics started right from the beginning of the campaign as Confederate and Mexican troops flooded into the Mesilla Valley. Most of the settlements in this region were outgrowths of US Army installations. The civilians were evacuated and anything that would have been of any worth to the enemy had long since been removed or destroyed. Nothing was heavily defended, and the pattern would repeat itself over and over. Confederate or Mexican troops would locate an enemy force; they would gather their strength and attack. The US troops would repulse one or two assaults and then withdraw.

The cycle would make Mexican Field Marshall Mariom declare one victory after another. The newspapers and politicians seemed to agree. Strangely enough, these "victories" were having an effect on the allied command structure that Pershing could have never predicted, but would take anyway. It was no secret to anyone that McDonald and Mariom never got along. McDonald was far more skeptical of these easy victories and seemed to see them for what they were. He could not convince his Mexican counterpart of this and as a result their strategies began to slowly diverge into two very separate war plans.

The most important of these strategies was Mariom's deployment of his cavalry. Initially, they had been used to closely shield his movements and guard his supply lines. With the enemy in full retreat, not only did Mariom rapidly move his infantry forward, but he sent the bulk of his lancers far to the west on raids along the American rail lines. This would have major consequences later on. For the time being, it caused a final rift with McDonald, who then moved most of his forces to the east of the river and, at that point, the single allied army became two. Then, Mariom finally reached San Acacia.

What McDonald had suspected all along, finally happened, when the Mexican Army reached the small village that was nestled in a bend on the western bank of the Rio Grande. It was an insignificant little place that might have had a population of fifty people before the invasion. At this point, it was nothing but a small collection of adobe huts and of no use to anyone. What was important was just to the north and easily within sight of the village. The bend in the river was flanked by marshy flats. Two large mesas dominated what was a narrow valley that the river lazily flowed through. To the west was broken desert with a series of gullies running down from some high ridges.

Pershing had been fortifying this position since before the invasion. He had rightly calculated how much time it would take him to mass most of his forces from their far-flung outposts. He knew this place was a natural choke point with beautiful fields of fire. His engineers had made sure that they were even better by the time that Mariom showed up. His artillery, which had seen little action before now, was set up on the reverse slope of the mesas. The peaks were manned by observers and machineguns which supported the infantry at the southern bases of the high ground. There was no getting around this position, and when the Mexican attacks tried to go through the defenses, something happened that Mariom did not expect.

The Americans did not leave.

The first two days of Mexican attacks went in with little artillery support as Mariom was still of the opinion that the Americans would not stay, and Mariom did not wish to slow down his rate of advance. After massive casualties, it became clear that a deliberate assault was needed, and Mariom would spend two more days planning this attack. By the time he launched it, the Americans had already switched to their alternate firing positions and it neutralized much of the effectiveness of the Mexican Artillery.

Mariom decided to wait until McDonald could catch up on the east bank. The Mexicans took those three days to reform their ranks, but US artillery gave them very little opportunity to make good on the time. Pershing also decided to launch several raids on Mexican lines as well. When McDonald finally reached the battle, the Mexican Army was not in any better shape. As a result, Mariom demanded that McDonald flank the position on the east bank, then cross the river north of the US positions. It took several days before that argument resulted in some kind of plan, and by that time, it was too late. Pershing had already redeployed to meet this very move.

McDonald suggested that they withdraw to the south and reform into a single unified force before attacking Pershing again. Mariom would hear nothing of it and demanded more action. As a result, after being stalled at San Acacia for two weeks, an impromptu attack was launched with the two allied armies being separated by the river. McDonald's move on the east side was halfhearted at best. His troops came up against artillery fire almost as soon as they began moving. The Mexicans were in no shape to launch the kind of attack that was needed. The end result was an early Confederate withdrawal and a Mexican assault that collapsed after only a half hour.

Pershing had stopped his enemy cold and dished out a lot more than he and taken. Even so, he was still outnumbered and lacked the firepower that was required to go over on the offensive. The immediate threat to Albuquerque was over, but a stalemate is a stalemate. Pershing was not sure how long both sides could wait the other out, and he was only now starting to see the effects of the Confederate re-supply system. Their trucks were outperforming US mules, and despite the tactical victory, Pershing might still lose. They were at a tipping point, and slowly Pershing began to realize the ultimate victory at San Acacia was going to have to come from somewhere else.

Silver City

The name has endured the test of time, and for that reason I have kept it. The battle that took place between the US and Mexican Cavalry, in early September of 1900, would become a media sensation for a lot of reasons and some have suggested that the name of this clash has a lot to do with why. Given the circumstances of the battle and who was involved, I doubt the validity of this and firmly believe the battle would have become front page news no matter what it was called. Still, the simple fact remains that the battle did not take place at Silver City, New Mexico. How it wound up with that name is anyone's guess. Many have suggested that reporters, most notably Richard Harding Davis, named it this because Bayard or Hurley simply did not conjure up the images that were desirable. This is possible, and I certainly would not put it past the media of the time, but it could be something as simple as their dispatches were filed from Silver City, after the fight.

The reality of the situation was that the series of running clashes that cumulated into a three hour-long stand-up fight took place on a series of ridges just south of the city of Bayard on the 1st of September 1900. It was nowhere near as intense or as long as the fight that Pershing had on his hands, and it is arguable that there was far less at stake. It was still an important battle. Its importance would ring far beyond the dusty slopes and even the overall campaign. The results of the battle would echo across the planet. Most of this was all due to one man, Theodore Roosevelt.

Colonel Roosevelt, with an ad hoc and under strength brigade of cavalry, was detached from General Funston's command in early August. Theoretically,

Brigadier Wood was in charge of the operation, but in all practical matters, Roosevelt had complete autonomy in the field. Roosevelt's mission was a simple one. He was to oppose the Mexican cavalry and minimize the damage they were doing to central New Mexico while he was to make every effort to keep them out of the western part of the state.

After the attack on Deming, in mid-August, it was quite clear that the local garrisons and militias would not be able to hold back Weygand and his Lancers. It was at this time that Roosevelt chose to deploy his forces forward and leave behind only token protection for the Prescott and Tombstone area. The first skirmishes happened within days, as it is clear that Weygand had not only detected this move but seemed to expect as much. Weygand had his own plan to deal with Roosevelt, and judging from the man's writings he was eager to do so. The fighting around Cananea had left Weygand with a sour taste in his mouth and he was most definitely looking for a rematch. This might have a lot to do with explaining why he had extended his forces so far west.

Weygand's most serious problem was his supply lines. While he carried enough ammunition with him and his raiding had provided his troopers with enough food and fodder, water was still a serious problem. Weygand had been heavily depending on the Confederate water trucks, but the further west he went the more ineffective they became since they were further from their own base of supplies. This was added to the fact that the main Mexican Army had now stalled out and were requiring the trucks in ever increasing numbers. These facts limited the time that Weygand could force a decision and he was acutely aware of this.

Roosevelt had been following the basic US plan as laid out by Pershing. He was avoiding a major engagement and he had his command spread thin as a result. As August came to an end it suddenly became clear to Roosevelt that Weygand was now becoming aggressive to the point of recklessness. At this time, Roosevelt made a command decision that was quite contrary to the overall spirit of operations. He was going to risk a real battle, because the situation had changed. There was no time to contact Pershing or even Funston. Roosevelt was the man on the scene, and he was taking a big gamble with his career and with the entire state.

The US Cavalry, mostly irregulars and draftees, began changing their campaign tactics. Roosevelt was metaphorically waiving a red flag in Weygand's face, tempting him to fight. Roosevelt also deliberately slowed his men's movements and allowed the Mexican Lancers to eventually catch up with them on that first day of September. At least it looked to Weygand as if the Roosevelt was slowing down. The reality was something entirely different.

Most of Roosevelt's men had spent their entire life on horseback. The majority of them had also spent their entire life in New Mexico. Roosevelt had the home field advantage, and this translated into a more in-depth knowledge of watering holes that were not well known or on any map. It allowed the American cavalry to take short cuts and traverse terrain that the Mexicans thought completely impossible in the hot sun of the late summer. While Roosevelt's small force was slowing down, other detachments under his command were doing the exact opposite. Roosevelt only concentrated enough troops to hold off a direct Mexican assault, or so he hoped. The rest of his troops were quickly headed for areas that were being vacated by the Mexican Lancers, who were also now trying to concentrate for a battle. By the first of September, Weygand had reeled in most of his command while most of Roosevelt's troopers were sweeping east towards the Mesilla valley.

Weygand's first moves on the battlefield that would come to be called The Battle of Silver City, were mostly recon missions so that the Mexican Lancers could count Roosevelt's guns. Weygand was much encouraged by the initial probes. He had the terrain working against him since Roosevelt had picked his ground well, but Weygand was clearly of the opinion that he had caught Roosevelt before he could bring his entire brigade together. Weygand had a lot of reason to believe this since he was well aware of how spread out the Americans were.

What Weygand was not aware of was that Roosevelt had intentionally limited the size of his force. He did not want Weygand to hesitate or wait for his own reserves to come up. Roosevelt was in effect dangling a carrot in front of the Mexicans. Weygand more than obliged his enemy. Not only was he worried about more American reinforcements arriving, but also his own men were critically short of water. The Lancers quickly launched an all-out attack on American lines.

The resulting attacks were a close-run thing, but Roosevelt's men were dug in, had good fields of fire, and had been reinforced by two batteries of field guns from the Colorado militia. This artillery had held its fire until the main assaults. As nasty a surprise as they were, Weygand had his own artillery and counter battery fire quickly negated the American surprise.

Ultimately, this brief fight would not be decided on this battlefield. The Mexicans took their lumps, but they were on the verge of breaking the American line when word arrived that their rear areas were being overrun and that communications with the main army had been cut. This affected the all too critical water situation, and Weygand was forced to break off his engagement and withdraw. He was not pleased, but had not given up either. Weygand was sure he would get another chance. Roosevelt was not playing his game.

Roosevelt switched right back to his hit and run tactics, only now his forces were not retreating after brief fights. They were sweeping further eastward, and this included the force he personally commanded at Silver City. Still using his secret weapon, detailed knowledge of the terrain, his forces began conducting ambushes on the retreating Lancers. After the first few fights, Weygand gave up trying to set up for a full-scale battle, and the Mexicans quickly learned not to pursue the Americans as they redeployed since another ambush often awaited the pursuit force. The Americans would give the Mexicans no rest, leave no source of water uncontested, and most important of all would savage the Mexican supply lines. Several Confederate trucks would also fall into American hands.

The orderly retreat of the weary and thirsty Mexican cavalry would degenerate into a route. Weygand's overly aggressive pursuit of Roosevelt would now become his undoing, as he found himself surrounded by what seemed to be an angry hornet's nest that he had stirred up. The retreat would turn into a head long rush to the alleged safety of the Mesilla Valley, and unfortunately for the allied forces stalled out in front of Pershing, this was also their base of supplies. Now, even Mariom would have to admit that a withdrawal was in order. The Mexican and Confederate armies would have to march back down the Rio Grande, and while they never left enemy territory, they found what they had occupied was little more than an empty desert valley of no worth to anyone. Any thoughts of resuming the offensive were now over.

From West Wing To West Wing

The victory in New Mexico should have been just the tonic needed by the campaign to re-elect President Root. It certainly could clinch the election if it were properly exploited. Initially, the US victories did hedge the polls back in Root's direction, but this election was still a very closely run thing. Root also had any number of other problems that had been dogging him since before the campaigning season. He also realized the victories handed him by Pershing and Roosevelt were not the October Surprise they needed to be, mostly because they did not happen in October. Most of the real fighting was over by that time, and Root was keenly aware that the voters had short memories. As Root examined his problems, he came to realize that in order for him to win reelection, he was going to have to make a bold move. All of his problems were coming to a single head, and as he saw it one man could solve all of them and that man's name was Theodore Roosevelt.

Root's main problem was first and foremost, his Vice President. Knox had been shoehorned in on the first election ticket because of the back room deals that were normal for the day. Root only approved of Knox because the man could serve to make the President look better. The only problem with Knox was that the man not only had a habit of getting into scandals, unfortunately for him they were well publicized ones. Hearst had harassed Knox to no end as it was obvious that the newspaper man, with his own presidential ambitions, saw Knox as Root's Achilles Heel. Hearst had made Knox out to be a buffoon and unfortunately for Knox, Root privately agreed with that assessment.

Most historians have come to agree that Knox was given a raw deal, but this meant little to Root with a reelection bid sitting on the horizon. This was why Knox was still the Vice President (his resignation was still waiting to be made public), but not Root's running mate for the election of November, 1900. As of yet, Root had not officially named a running mate even though it was widely accepted, by this time, that Senator William McKinley would most likely serve as the new Vice President. Now Root saw an opportunity to take care of multiple problems with one swift stroke.

Not only was the young and energetic Roosevelt a national hero, not only had he already managed to thwart the ambitions of Randolph Hearst, he was also a serious pain in the ass for Root. Roosevelt was seen by many of Root's supporters as a threat to their jobs. That was how Roosevelt had been side lined to New Mexico in the first place. At the time of Roosevelt's appointment, no one had ever thought that it would turn into such a heavily publicized theater of war. Now that it had, and Roosevelt's friends in the media had made him into a hero, why not use that? All the while Root got to put his chief rival in a position where he could keep an eye on him and minimize the damage the man could do. It would also be an effective way of keeping the September war victories in the public eye.

This was how Roosevelt went from the battlefield of war to the campaign of politics and in very short order. It had been printed that Roosevelt had accepted the nomination for Vice President before Roosevelt himself had even been notified that he was on the ticket. As Roosevelt would write in his journal, he saw it as an order from the commander in chief and he was a soldier, so he accepted the nomination even if he really wished to remain at the front.

Root, a shrewd politician, had calculated the situation well. He was correct in most aspects of his appraisal. Roosevelt's presence on the ticket, along with his energetic campaigning on the stump, shifted the polls in Root's favor and by November it was obvious who would win the election. What Root had been completely wrong about was his ability to constrain Roosevelt who was, after all, a man seething with ambition and the talent to go with it. Right from the start, it was obvious that Roosevelt not only had his own agenda, but Root could not temper it in anyway. All of this was before the Republicans sent Debbs and his Populists down in flames in the election. What would happen after Roosevelt was sworn in was even more serious in the eyes of Root. Then, something out of the blue would change the entire situation and alter the course of human history.

The events that would really unleash Roosevelt were still in the future. For the time being, it meant that the United States would remain in the war and this was all that concerned the governments in Paris and St. Petersburg. The Triple Entente had taken its lumps in the past year, but they had also managed some victories. Unfortunately for the world, the only thing that had really changed after another bloody year of war was, nothing at all. By the start of the new century no one was any closer to concluding let alone winning the war. The men running this conflict were getting desperate and they all slowly came to realize it was going to take something unseen to shift the balance to one side or the other. It would come and none of them would see it until it was long over.

To Be Continued.